Are You Ready to be an #NPin5Minutes?

This is a clinical review created to help guide you through the System PowerPoints found in the Bronze Max Bundle. Of course, these System Outlines are also a standalone, comprehensive clinical review to prepare you for your Nurse Practitioner certification exam - but trust us when we say you will maximize your studying success by pairing it with the Bronze Max Bundle.

Why should you trust us? Great question! Since the initial LWES launch, we have supported over hundreds of thousands of students as they crossed the NP threshold, and do not plan on stopping any time soon. Students who utilize our certification review memberships have a 98% pass rate, so whether you are studying for boards, planning to retest, or renewing your certification – you are in the right place.

How To Use:

1. Grab your favorite writing utensil, all the highlighters, and snacks.
2. Review the Bronze Max Bundle System PowerPoints either with, or without voiceover (your choice) alongside your System Outlines. Take notes, highlight to your heart's desire, and write down any buzzwords you find!
3. Complete the Bronze Clinical Crash Course to tie everything together. This crash course will serve as the icing on the cake.
4. Participate in a Live Review with Professor Walden or test your knowledge with our Practice Question Test Bank.
5. Once you receive your 'I PASSED!' paper post-exam, submit your testimony to our #NPin5Minutes page on our website to share the good news!

If you have any questions or need help developing a study plan, email us at info@latrinawaldenexamsolutions.com – we'll help steer you in the right direction. We look forward to your future success and cannot wait to celebrate with you. Happy studying!

Sincerely,

Professor Walden & Team LWES

Terms of Service

Published in Stone Mountain, GA in 2021 by Latrina Walden Exam Solutions

Copyrighted © 2021. All Rights Reserved.

ISBN: 978-1-7369010-0-7

First Edition. Printed and bound in the United States.

Table of Contents

CARDIOVASCULAR

CARDIOVASCULAR

Definition of Holosystolic Murmur
- _____

Definition of Pansystolic Murmur
- _____

Most Common Causes of Pansystolic Murmur
- _____
- _____
- _____

MYOCARDIAL INFARCTION (MI)

Definition of Myocardial Infarction (MI)
- _____
- _____

Meaning of Myo, Cardial, and Infarction?
- Myo: _____
- Cardial: _____
- Infarction: _____

Medication Causing Heartburn:
- _____
- _____
- _____

Damage and Death to Heart Tissue
- By graphical presentation

Signs and Symptoms of Myocardial Infarction (MI)
- _____
- _____
- _____
- _____
- _____

Notes

SYSTOLIC MURMURS

What are Systolic Murmurs?
- _____

What is Mitral Regurgitation?
- . _____
    - Time- _____
    - Location- _____
    - Best Heard- _____
    - Characteristics- _____
    - Associated Symptoms- _____

What is Aortic Stenosis?
- _____
    - Time- _____
    - Location- _____
    - Best Heard- _____
    - Characteristics- _____
    - Associated Symptoms- _____

MITRAL REGURGITATION

What is Mitral Regurgitation?
- _____

Location of Mitral Regurgitation
- _____
- _____

Notes

AORTIC STENOSIS

Definition of Aortic Stenosis
- _____
- _____

Causes of Aortic Stenosis
- _____

Location of Aortic Stenosis
- _____
- _____

TRICUSPID REGURGITATION

What is Tricuspid Regurgitation?
- _____
- _____

Causes of Tricuspid Regurgitation
- _____
- _____

A Short Overview of Tricuspid Regurgitation
- Time- _____
- Location- _____
- Best Heard- _____
- Characteristics- _____
- Associated Symptom- _____

Notes

MVP

What is MVP?
- _____
- _____

Location of MVP
- _____

Difference Between Normal Heart and Mitral Valve Prolapse
- _____

MITRAL STENOSIS (DIASTOLIC MURMUR)

What is Mitral Stenosis (Diastolic Murmur)?
- _____

Characteristic of Mitral Stenosis (Diastolic Murmur)?
- _____

Location of Mitral Stenosis (Diastolic Murmur)
- _____

Difference between Normal Mitral Valve and Narrowing Mitral Valve (Mitral Valve Stenosis)
- _____

Difference between Mitral Valve Stenosis and Mitral Valve Regurgitation
- _____

Definition of Mitral Valve Regurgitation:

_____

_____

Notes

CARDIOVASCULAR

AORTIC REGURGITATION

Definition of Aortic Regurgitation
- _____
- _____

Characteristics of Aortic Regurgitation
- _____

Introduction of Normal Valve Operation and Leakage of Valve
- Normal Valve Operation- _____
- Leakage of Valve- _____

TRICUSPID STENOSIS

Where are Diastolic Murmurs Best Heard?
- _____

Causes of Tricuspid Stenosis
- _____
- _____

Definition of Tricuspid Stenosis?
- _____

Time of Tricuspid Stenosis
- _____

Location of Tricuspid Stenosis
Left 2ⁿᵈ, 3ʳᵈ inter costal space

Where is Tricuspid Stenosis Best Heard?
- _____

Notes

Characteristics of Tricuspid Stenosis
- _____

Associated Symptoms of Tricuspid Stenosis
- _____

Use of Stethoscope
- _____

All Diastolic Murmurs are Pathological
- Murmurs I = _____
- Murmurs II = _____
- Murmurs III = _____
- Murmurs IV = _____
- Murmurs V = _____
- Murmurs VI = _____

BENIGN SPLIT S2

When is a Benign Split S2 Heard?
- _____

What is Benign Split S2?
- _____
  _____

Associated Symptoms of Benign Split S2
- _____
- _____
- _____
- _____

Best for Benign Split S2
- _____

Characteristics of Benign Split S2
- _____
- _____

Notes

CARDIOVASCULAR

S3 – HF

What is the meaning of S3 – HF

- _____

What Occurs in S3 – HF
- _____

Effects of S3 – HF
- _____

Time of S3 – HF
- Kentucky
- Early diastole

Characteristics of S3 – HF
- _____

Where is S3 Best Heard?
- _____

S4 – LVH

What is Left Ventricular Hypertrophy (LVH)
- _____

Meaning of S4
- _____

Characteristic of S4 – LVH
- _____

Notes

Difference between Inaudible S4 (Normal) and Audible S4 (Usually Abnormal)
- _____

Effects of S4 – LVH
- _____
- _____
- _____
- _____

S1 AND S2

How Can I Hear the S1 and S2 Sounds Best?
- _____

Where is S1 Best Heard?

- _____

Where is S2 Best Heard?
- _____

The major sounds
- The two major sounds of the normal heart sound like "lub dub."
    - _____
    - _____

ISOLATED SYSTOLIC HYPERTENSION

Definition of Isolated Systolic Hypertension
- _____
  _____

Notes

Cause of Isolated Systolic Hypertension
- _____

Common age of Isolated Systolic Hypertension
- _____

Characteristic of Isolated Systolic Hypertension
- _____
- _____
- _____

Feature of Hypertension
- Systolic
  - _____
- Diastolic
  - _____

Secondary Diseases of Hypertension
- _____
- Coronary atherosclerosis
  - _____
  - _____
- _____
- Atherosclerosis of cerebral vessels
  - _____
- _____
- Atherosclerosis of renal vessels
  - _____

Treatment of Isolated Systolic Hypertension
1. Primary drugs:
   - _____
     - _____
     - _____
2. Secondary drugs:
   - _____
   - _____
3. Calcium channel
   - _____

Notes

CARDIOVASCULAR

STABLE ANGINA

Definition of Stable Angina?
*   _____

Effect of Stable Angina
*   _____

Diagnosis of Stable Angina
*   Stress test
    *   _____

Treatment of Stable Angina
*   _____

PERIPHERAL VASCULAR DISEASE (PVD)

Difference Between Arterial and Venous

Arterial	Venous
Intermittent Claudication Pain	Dull, Achey Pain
No Edema	Lower Leg Edema
No Pulse or Weak Pulse No Drainage	Pulse Present Drainage
Round, Smooth Sores	Sores with Irregular Borders
Black Eschar	Yellow Slough or Ruddy Skin
Location of Sores: Toes and Feet	Location of Sores: Ankles

Notes

Latrina Walden™
Exam Solutions

Basic Treatment at Home
- _____

Medications for PVD
- TX: _____
- Surgical TX: _____

Sign of Peripheral Vascular Disease
- _____

Diagnosis of Peripheral Vascular Disease (PVD)
- Venous Insufficiency
    - _____
    - _____
    - _____
    - _____
    - _____
- PAD
    - _____
    - _____
    - _____
    - _____
    - _____
    - _____

Effect of Peripheral Vascular Disease (PVD)
- _____

Thiazides
- Causes
    - _____
    - _____
    - _____
    - _____
    - _____
    - _____

Notes

CARDIOVASCULAR

INFECTIVE ENDOCARDITIS

Infection of this Certain Area of the Heart

- _____
- _____
- _____

What does Endocarditis look like?

- _____

Effects of Infective Endocarditis

- _____
- _____
- _____
- _____
- _____
- _____

Symptoms of Infective Endocarditis

- _____
- _____
- _____
- _____
- _____
- _____
- _____
- _____

Treatment of Infective Endocarditis

- _____
- _____
- _____
- _____

PULSUS PARADOXUS

Definition of Pulsus Paradoxus

- _____

Best Way to Hear Pulsus Paradoxus

- _____

Notes

Effect of Pulsus Paradoxus
- _____

Symptoms of Pulsus Paradoxus
- _____

Treatment
- This is a clinical finding!!
    - _____
    - i.e. _____

Things you should know
- _____
- _____
- _____
- _____
- _____
- _____
- _____
- _____
- _____
- _____
- _____
- _____
- _____
- _____
- **Avoid** _____
- **Avoid** _____
- **Avoid** _____
- **Avoid** _____
- **Avoid** _____
- **Avoid** _____
- **Avoid** _____
- _____
- _____
- _____
- _____

Notes

CARDIOVASCULAR

Notes

_____

_____

_____

_____

_____

_____

_____

_____

_____

_____

_____

_____

_____

_____

_____

_____

_____

_____

_____

_____

_____

_____

_____

_____

_____

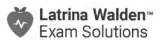
ENDOCRINE

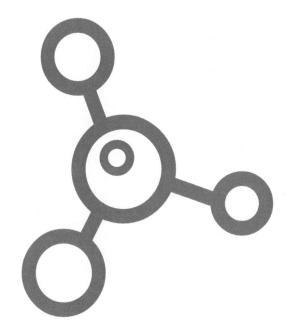

HYPOTHYROIDISM

Definition of Hypothyroidism
- _____

Causes of Hypothyroidism
- _____
- _____

Symptoms of Hypothyroidism
- _____
- _____
- _____
- _____
- _____

Causes of Hypothyroidism
- _____
- _____
- _____
- _____
- _____

Diagnosis of Hypothyroidism
- _____
- _____
- _____

Treatment of Hypothyroidism
- _____

HYPERTHYROIDISM

Definition of Hyperthyroidism
- _____
  _____

Notes

Symptoms of Hyperthyroidism
- The symptoms of hyperthyroidism include the following:
    - _____
    - _____
    - _____
    - _____
    - _____
    - _____
    - _____

Causes of Hyperthyroidism
- _____
- _____
- _____

Diagnosis of Hyperthyroidism
- _____
  _____

Treatment of Hyperthyroidism
- _____
- _____
- _____
- _____
    - _____

GRAVES' DISEASE

Definition of Graves' Disease
- _____
  _____

Symptoms of Graves' Disease
- _____
- _____
- _____
- _____
- _____
- _____
- _____

Notes

Diagnosis of Graves' Disease

- _____
- Lab tests to measure the amount of thyroid hormones in the blood include:
    - _____
    - _____
    - _____

Treatment of Graves' Disease

- _____

    - _____

DIABETES

Introduction to Diabetes

- _____
  _____
- _____
  _____
- _____
  _____

Types of Diabetes
- There are three major types of diabetes
    - _____
    - _____
    - _____

Type 1 Diabetes

- Definition of Type 1 Diabetes
    - _____

- Caused by Type 1 Diabetes
    - _____

Notes

- Characteristic of Type 1 Diabetes
  - _____

- Common Age of Type 1 Diabetes
  - _____

- Symptoms of Type 1 Diabetes (3 P'S)
  - _____
  - _____
  - _____

- Diagnosis of Type 1 Diabetes
  - _____
  - _____
  - _____

- Treatment of Type 1 Diabetes
  - _____
  - _____
  - _____
  - _____
  - _____

Type 2 Diabetes

- Definition of Type 2 Diabetes
  - _____

- Characteristic of Type 2 Diabetes
  - _____

Notes

- Symptoms of Type 2 Diabetes (3 P'S)
  - _____
  - _____
  - _____

- Risk Factor and Prevention of Type 2 Diabetes
  - Age: _____
  - Family: _____
  - Ethnicity: _____

- Other Risk Factors of Type 2 Diabetes
  - _____
  - _____
  - _____
  - _____

- Diagnosis of Type 2 Diabetes
  - Type 2 diabetes may remain undetected for many years and the diagnosis is often made when a complication appears or a routine blood or urine glucose test is done
    - _____
    - _____
    - _____
    - _____

- Characteristic of Type 2 Diabetes
  - Diabetes
    - HbA1c (percent)
      - _____
    - Fasting Plasma Glucose (mg/dL)
      - _____
    - Oral Glucose Tolerance Test (mg/dL)
      - _____

Notes

- PRA Diabetes
    - HbA1c (percent)
        - _____
    - Fasting Plasma Glucose (mg/dL)
        - _____
    - Oral Glucose Tolerance Test (mg/dL)
        - _____
- Normal
    - HbA1c (percent)
        - _____
    - Fasting Plasma Glucose (mg/dL)
        - _____
    - Oral Glucose Tolerance Test (mg/dL)
        - _____
- Treatment of Type 2 Diabetes
    - _____
      _____
    - Examples of possible treatments for Type 2 Diabetes include:
        - _____
        - _____
        - _____
        - _____
    - _____ Therapy
        - _____
          _____
    - *Start when* _____

Notes

METABOLIC SYNDROME

Definition of Metabolic Syndrome
- _____
  _____

Occurrence of Metabolic Syndrome
- _____
- _____
- _____
- _____

Symptoms of Metabolic Syndrome
- _____
  _____

Causes of Metabolic Syndrome
- _____

Risk Factors of Metabolic Syndrome
- _____
- _____
- _____
- _____

Diagnosis of Metabolic Syndrome
- _____
- _____
- _____
- _____

** **You Need 3 = Metabolic Syndrome**

Notes

ENDOCRINE

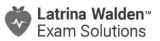
Management of Macular Degeneration

- Lifestyle Changes Include
    - _____
    - _____
    - _____
    - _____

PITUITARY GLAND DISORDERS

Definition of Pituitary Gland Disorders
- _____
  _____

What Does it Look Like?
- _____

Disorders
- Pituitary Tumors: _____
- These tumors are _____ in adults
- It is also called _____
- The problems caused by pituitary tumors fall into three general categories
    - Hypersecretion: _____
    - Hyposecretion: _____
    - Tumor mass effects: _____
- It can result in hormonal overproduction causing serious endocrine disturbances such as:
    - _____
    - _____
    - _____

Notes

Symptoms of Pituitary Gland Disorders

- GH
    - *Children:* _____
    - *Adults:* _____

- LH/FSH

    - _____
      _____

- ACTH

    - _____

- TSH
    - _____

- Prolactin
    - _____

- Vasopressin (ADH)
    - _____

Treatment of Pituitary Gland Disorders

- GH
    - _____

- LH/FSH

    - *Men:* _____

    - *Women:* _____

- ACTH

    - _____

- TSH
    - _____
      _____

- Prolactin
    - _____

- Vasopressin (ADH)
    - _____

Notes

ENDOCRINE

ADDISON'S DISEASE

Introduction to Addison's Disease
- Definition of Addison's Disease
  - _____
    _____
- Impact
  - _____
- Another Name
  - _____

Signs and Symptoms of Addison's Disease
- Fatigue
  - _____
  - _____
  - _____
  - _____
- Loss of appetite
  - _____

Causes of Addison's Disease
- _____
- _____
- _____
- _____
- _____

Diagnosis of Addison's Disease
- _____
- _____

Other Tests of Addison's Disease

Other tests include computed tomography (CT) scans and magnetic resonance imaging (MRI) – pituitary gland

Treatment of Addison's Disease
- _____
  - _____
  - _____

Notes

CUSHING'S SYNDROME

Definition of Cushing's Syndrome
- _____
  _____

Difference between Healthy and Cushing's Syndrome
- _____

Complications of Cushing's Syndrome
- _____
- _____
- _____
- _____
- _____
- _____
- _____
- _____
- _____
- _____
- _____

Causes and Risk Factors of Cushing's Syndrome
- _____
- _____
- _____
- _____
- _____

Signs and Symptoms of Cushing's Syndrome
- _____
- _____
- _____
- _____
- _____
- _____

Notes

Impact of Cushing's Syndrome

- _____
- _____
- _____
- _____
- _____
- Males
  - _____
- _____
- _____
- _____
- Females:
  - _____
  - _____
- _____
- _____
- _____
- _____

Causes of Cushing's Syndrome
- _____

Diagnosis of Cushing's Syndrome
- _____
- _____
- _____
- _____

Treatment of Cushing's Syndrome
- _____

LUPUS

Definition of Lupus
- _____
  _____

Characteristics of Lupus
- _____

Notes

Types of Lupus

- _____
- _____
- _____
- _____
- _____

Symptoms of Lupus

- _____
- _____
- _____
- _____
- _____
- _____
- _____
- _____
- _____

Complications of Lupus

- _____
- _____
- _____

Diagnosis of Lupus

- Blood tests
  - _____
  - _____
  - _____

- Urine tests
  - _____

Treatment of Lupus

- _____
- Medications:
  - _____

Notes

POLYCYSTIC OVARY SYNDROME

Definition of Polycystic Ovary Syndrome
- _____
  _____

Characteristic of Polycystic Ovary Syndrome
- _____

What Does Polycystic Ovary Syndrome Look Like?
- _____

Causes of Polycystic Ovary Syndrome
- _____
  _____

Symptoms of Polycystic Ovary Syndrome
- _____
- _____
- _____
- _____
- _____
- _____
- _____

Complications of Polycystic Ovary Syndrome
- _____
- _____
- _____
- _____
- _____
- _____
- _____
- _____
- _____

Notes

Diagnosis of Polycystic Ovary Syndrome

- _____
- _____
- _____
- _____

Treatment of Polycystic Ovary Syndrome

- _____
- _____
- Medications:
    - _____
    - _____
    - _____

Notes

Notes

_____

_____

_____

_____

_____

_____

_____

_____

_____

_____

_____

_____

_____

_____

_____

_____

_____

_____

_____

_____

_____

_____

_____

_____

_____

_____

_____

GASTROENTEROLOGY

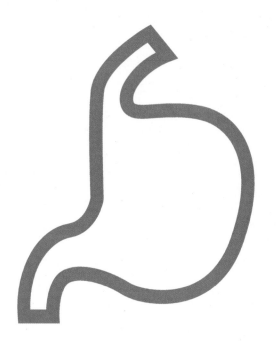

Gastroesophageal Reflux Disease (GERD)

- An overview Gastroesophageal Reflux Disease (GERD)
    - _____
      _____

- GERD Sufferer
- What is Etiology?
    - _____
- Diagnostic
    - _____
        - When endoscopy is being used?
    - _____
    - _____
    - _____
- Symptoms of GERD
    - Mouth
        1. _____
        2. _____
        3. _____
    - Ears
        1. _____
    - Chest
        1. _____
        2. _____
        3. _____
    - Throat
        1. _____
        2. _____
        3. _____
        4. _____
        5. _____
        6. _____
    - Abdomen
        1. _____

Notes

- How Can You Treat GERD by Changing Lifestyle?
    - _____
    - _____
    - _____
    - _____
    - _____
    - _____
    - _____
    - _____
    - _____
    - _____

- Treatment
    - Proton pump inhibitors (PPI's)
        - _____
        - _____
        - _____
        - _____
    - _____
    - _____
    - _____

Peptic Ulcer Disease

- Causes of Peptic Ulcer Disease
    - _____
    - _____
    - _____
    - _____
    - _____
- Common Patients of Peptic Ulcer Disease

Notes

- Symptoms of Peptic Ulcer Disease
  - Gastric
    1. _____
  - Duodenal
    1. Pain presents 2-5 hours after meals and late at night
       _____
    2. More food and antacids relieve the pain
       _____
  - Epigastric Tenderness _____

Diagnosis and Treatment
  - EGD/H pylori testing
    - Lifestyle _____
    - (H2, PPI, Sucralfate) _____
    - H pylori _____
- Zollinger-Ellison Syndrome
  - How can Gastrinomas Develop?
  - Causes of Zollinger-Ellison Syndrome
    - _____
  - Dx of Zollinger-Ellison Syndrome
    - _____
  - Treatment of Zollinger-Ellison Syndrome
    - _____
    - _____
    - _____

Inflammatory Bowel Disease

- An Overview of Inflammatory Bowel Disease
  - Chron's = _____
  - Ulcerative colitis = _____

Notes

- Symptoms of Inflammatory Bowel Disease
  - Chron's Disease
    - _____
    - _____
    - _____
    - _____
    - _____
  - Ulcerative Colitis
    - _____
    - _____
    - _____
    - _____

Physical Exam Findings
  - Chron's Disease
    - _____
    - _____
    - _____
    - _____
    - _____
  - Ulcerative Colitis
    - _____

Diagnosis and Treatment
  - Chron's Disease
    - _____
    - _____
    - _____
  - Ulcerative Colitis
    - _____
    - _____
  - High Fiber Diet/ Probiotics
  - Medications
    - _____

Notes

Irritable Bowel Syndrome

- An overview of Irritable Bowel Syndrome
  - _____
    _____

- Symptoms of Irritable Bowel Syndrome
  - _____
  - _____
  - _____
  - _____
  - _____
  - _____

- Diagnosis and Treatment
  - Labs: _____
    - _____
    - _____
    - _____

Notes

Notes

GENITOURINARY

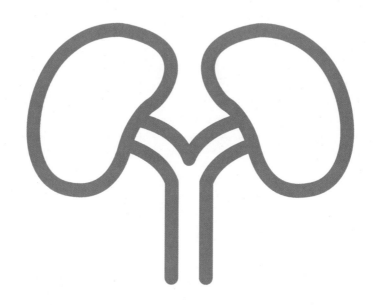

URINARY TRACT INFECTION (UTI)

Definition of Urinary Tract Infection (UTI)
- _____
  _____

Most Common Causative Organism
- _____
- _____

Common Symptoms of Urinary tract infection (UTI)
- _____
- _____
- _____

Urinary Tract Anatomy
- _____
- _____
- _____
- Cross section
  - _____
  - _____
  - _____
- Infected urine
  - _____
  - _____

Signs of Urinary Tract Infection
- _____
- _____
- _____
- _____

Treatment of Urinary Tract Infection
- _____
- _____
- _____

Notes

PYELONEPHRITIS

Definition of Pyelonephritis
- _____
_____

Caused by
- _____

Overview of Pyelonephritis
- _____
- _____

Most Common Symptoms of Pyelonephritis
- _____
- _____
- _____
- _____
- _____
- _____

Diagnostic Lab of Pyelonephritis
- UA with **WBC Casts present**
  - _____

Treatment of Pyelonephritis
- _____
- _____
- _____
- _____
- _____

NEPHROLITHIASIS

Definition of Nephrolithiasis
- _____
_____

Overview of Nephrolithiasis
- _____

Most Common Symptoms of Nephrolithiasis
- _____
- _____
- _____

Notes

Diagnostic Lab of Nephrolithiasis

- _____
- UA: _____
- _____
- _____
- _____

  CHECK PTH

Treatment of Nephrolithiasis

- _____
- _____
- If fluid intake does not prevent stones:
  - _____
  - _____
- Contrary to popular belief: _____

CHRONIC KIDNEY DISEASE

Definition of Chronic Kidney Disease

- _____
- _____
- _____

High Risk Patients

- _____
- _____
- _____
- _____
- _____
- _____
- _____

Stages of Chronic Kidney Disease
- Stage 1: _____
  - GFR: _____
  - %of kidney function: _____
- Stage 2: _____
  - GFR: _____
  - %of kidney function: _____

Notes

- Stage 3a: _____
  - GFR: _____
  - %of kidney function: _____
- Stage 3b: _____
  - GFR: _____
- %of kidney function: _____

  - Stage 4: _____
    - GFR: _____
    - %of kidney function: _____

- Stage 5: _____
  - GFR: _____
  - %of kidney function: _____

Chronic Renal Failure (CRF)

- _____
- _____
- _____
- _____
- _____
- _____
- _____
- _____
- _____
- _____

Complications

- Normal
  - _____
  - _____
  - _____
  - _____
- Damage
  - _____
  - _____
  - _____
- GFR
  - _____
  - _____
  - _____
- Kidney failure
  - _____
- Death

Notes

Diagnostic Test of Chronic Kidney Disease

- _____
- _____
- _____

Treatment of Chronic Kidney Disease

- _____
- _____
- _____
- _____

BENIGN PROSTATIC HYPERPLASIA (BPH)

Definition of Benign Prostatic hyperplasia (BPH)

- _____
  _____

Signs and Symptoms of Benign Prostatic hyperplasia (BPH)

- _____
- _____
- _____
- _____
- _____

Difference between Normal and Enlarged Prostate

- _____

Treatment of Benign Prostatic hyperplasia (BPH)

- _____
- _____
- _____

Another Treatment of Benign Prostatic hyperplasia (BPH)

- Saw palmetto extract
  - _____
  - _____
  - _____

Notes

PSA- PROSTATE SPECIFIC ANTIGEN

Definition of PSA- Prostate Specific Antigen
- _____
  _____

Diagnostic Test of PSA- Prostate Specific Antigen
- Tx: _____
- USPSTF recommends screening _____
  - Stop screening above age _____

Treatment of PSA- Prostate Specific Antigen
- DRUG CLASS FOR TX OF BPH
  - _____
  - _____

Important Information
- UA with Protein? → _____ →
  _____
- Uncomplicated UTI: _____
- UTI in pregnant (always treat R/F Pyelonephritis) –1st line Macrobid, not in _____ trimester! →
  _____
- WBC casts in urine= _____
- UA: _____
- Large amount of epithelial cells? _____

Notes

HEAD, EARS, EYES, NOSE, THROAT

NOSEBLEED

Causes of Nosebleed
- Snorting cocaine produces a longer high than injecting it, but it can damage
  - _____
  - _____
- As well as cause
  - _____
  - _____

Most Common Abused Drug
- _____

Effect of Snort Cocaine
- _____

ACUTE VIRAL RHINOSINUSITIS (AVRS)

What is Acute Rhinosinusitis?
- _____
  _____

Causes of Acute Viral Rhinosinusitis (AVRS)
- _____
- _____
- _____
- _____

Signs and Symptoms of Acute Viral Rhinosinusitis (AVRS)
- _____
- _____
- _____

Diagnosis of Acute Viral Rhinosinusitis (AVRS)
- _____
- _____
- _____
- _____
- _____

Notes

- _____
- Symptomatic tx: _____
- First line: _____
- Allergy to PCN/Cephalosporin: _____

Concerns of Acute Viral Rhinosinusitis (AVRS)

- _____
- _____
- _____

EYES

HERPES KERATITIS

Causes of Herpes Keratitis

- _____
  _____

Signs and Symptoms of Herpes Keratitis

- _____
- _____
- _____
- Herpes Zoster Ophthalmicus → _____

Diagnosis of Herpes Keratitis

- _____
- _____

Treatment of Herpes Keratitis

- _____

Concerns of Herpes Keratitis

- _____

CORNEAL ABRASIONS

Introduction of Corneal Abrasions

- _____
- _____

Notes

Corneal Abrasions can be Caused by:

- _____
- _____
- _____
- _____

Examination of Corneal Abrasions
- On the examination of the eye, the patient observes: _____
_____

Causes of Corneal Abrasions

- _____
- _____
- _____
- _____

Contact Lenses

- _____

MACULAR DEGENERATION

Definition of Macular Degeneration
- _____
_____

Impact of Macular Degeneration
- _____
_____

Causes of Macular Degeneration
- _____

Signs and Symptoms of Macular Degeneration

- _____
- _____
- _____
- _____

Treatment of Macular Degeneration

- _____
- _____

Notes

Concerns of Macular Degeneration
- _____
- _____
- _____

Difference Between Healthy Eye and MD
- _____

AGE-RELATED MACULAR DEGENERATION

Definition of Age-Related Macular Degeneration
- _____
  _____

Characteristic of Age-Related Macular Degeneration
- _____

Symptoms of Age-Related Macular Degeneration
- _____
- _____

Treatment of Age-Related Macular Degeneration
- _____

ACUTE ANGLE CLOSURE GLAUCOMA

Definition of Acute Angle Closure Glaucoma
- _____
  _____

Signs and Symptoms of Acute Angle Closure Glaucoma
- _____
- _____
- _____

Examination of Acute Angle Closure Glaucoma
- _____
- _____
- _____
- _____

Notes

What Things Trigger Glaucoma?

- _____
- _____
- _____

Diagnosis of Acute Angle Closure Glaucoma

- _____
- _____
- _____

Treatment of Acute Angle Closure Glaucoma

- _____

Concerns of Acute Angle Closure Glaucoma

- _____
- _____
- _____

PRIMARY OPEN ANGLE GLAUCOMA

Definition of Primary Open Angle Glaucoma

- _____
_____

Characteristic of Primary Open Angle Glaucoma

- _____
_____

Impact of Primary Open Angle Glaucoma

- _____

Notes

Causes and Risk Factors of Primary Open Angle Glaucoma

- _____
- _____
- _____
- _____
- _____

Signs and Symptoms of Primary Open Angle Glaucoma

- _____
  _____
- _____
- _____

Treatment of Primary Open Angle Glaucoma

- _____
- _____
- _____
- _____
- _____
- _____
- _____
- _____

Concerns of Primary Open Angle Glaucoma

- _____
- _____
- _____
- _____

What Does Primary Open Angle Glaucoma Look Like?

- _____

CATARACTS

Definition of Cataracts

- _____
  _____

Characteristic of Cataracts

- _____

Causes of Cataracts

- _____

Notes

Difference Between Normal Eye and Cataracts Eye
- Normal Eye:
    - _____
- Cataracts Eye:
    - _____

RETINAL DETACHMENT

Definition of Retinal Detachment
- _____
  _____

Causes of Retinal Detachment
- _____

Retinal Detachment can be Caused by
- _____
- _____
- _____

Characteristic of Retinal Detachment
- _____

Risk Factors of Retinal Detachment
- _____
- _____
- _____
- _____
- _____
- _____

Sign and Symptoms of Retinal Detachment
- _____
  _____
- _____

Treatment of Retinal Detachment
- _____

Notes

PAPILLEDEMA

Definition of Papilledema
- _____
  _____

Characteristic of Papilledema
- _____

Causes of Papilledema
- _____
- _____
- _____
- _____

Difference between Papilledema and Normal Optic Disk
- _____

HYPERTENSIVE RETINOPATHY

Definition of Hypertensive Retinopathy
- _____
  _____

Causes of Hypertensive Retinopathy
- _____

Hypertensive Can be Caused by
- _____

Examination of Hypertensive Retinopathy
- On examination, the following abnormalities can be seen:
  - _____
  - _____
  - _____

DIABETIC RETINOPATHY

Definition of Diabetic Retinopathy
- _____
  _____

Notes

Impact of Diabetic Retinopathy
- _____

Symptoms or Appearance of Diabetic Retinopathy
- _____
- _____

Difference Between Normal Eye and Diabetic Retinopathy
- _____

HORDEOLUM

Definition of Hordeolum
- _____
  _____

Causes of Hordeolum
- _____

Characteristic of Hordeolum
- _____

Signs and Symptoms of Hordeolum
- _____
- _____
- _____

Treatment of Hordeolum
- _____
- _____
- _____

Notes

CHALAZION

Causes of Chalazion

Abscess of hair follicle and sebaceous gland in upper or lower lid

Internal inflammation of meibomian gland

Signs and Symptoms of Chalazion
- _____
- _____

Treatment of Chalazion
- _____
- _____

Concerns of Chalazion
- _____

Difference Between Hordeolum and Chalazion
- Hordeolum
  - _____
  - _____
  - _____
- Chalazion
  - _____
  - _____

XANTHELASMA

Definition of Xanthelasma
- _____
  _____

Symptoms of Xanthelasma
- _____

Notes

Treatment of Xanthelasma
- _____

Diagnosis of Xanthelasma
- _____
- _____

ANTERIOR UVEITIS (IRITIS)

Definition of Anterior Uveitis (IRITIS)
- _____

Causes of Anterior Uveitis (IRITIS)
- _____
  _____

PERIORBITAL CELLULITIS

Definition of Periorbital Cellulitis
- _____

Causes of Periorbital Cellulitis
- _____
  _____

ALLERGIC CONJUNCTIVITIS

Cause of Allergic Conjunctivitis
- _____

Signs and Symptoms of Allergic Conjunctivitis
- _____
- _____
- _____
- _____
- _____

Notes

Treatment of Allergic Conjunctivitis
- _____
- _____
- _____
- _____

Concerns of Allergic Conjunctivitis
- _____

BACTERIAL/VIRAL CONJUNCTIVITIS

Introduction of Bacterial/Viral Conjunctivitis
- Viral: _____
- Viruses: _____

Causes of Bacterial/Viral Conjunctivitis
- SSX: _____
- Watery discharge _____
- Photophobia _____

What Does It Look Like?
- _____
- _____
- _____

Signs and Symptoms of Bacterial/Viral Conjunctivitis
- Bacterial (SSX):
    - _____
    - _____
    - _____
    - _____

Causes of Bacterial/Viral Conjunctivitis
- _____
- _____
- _____

Treatment of Bacterial/Viral Conjunctivitis
- TX: _____

Notes

ARCUS SENILIS

Definition of Arcus Senilis
- _____

An Overview of Arcus Senilis
- _____

Characteristic of Arcus Senilis
- _____

Common Age of Arcus Senilis
- _____

OPTIC NEURITIS

Causes of Optic Neuritis
- Multiple sclerosis _____

Signs and Symptoms of Optic Neuritis
- _____
  _____

- _____
- _____

Difference between Normal and Optic Neuritis
- _____

Treatment of Optic Neuritis
- _____

PINGUECULA

Causes of Pinguecula
- _____

Signs and Symptoms of Pinguecula
- _____

Notes

Treatment of Pinguecula
- _____
- _____
- _____
- _____

Diagnostics of Pinguecula
- _____

PTERYGIUM

Causes of Pterygium
- Chronic sun exposure _____

Signs and Symptoms of Pterygium
- _____
- _____
- _____
- _____
- _____

Treatment of Pterygium
- _____
- _____
- _____

Diagnostics of Pterygium
- _____

SUBCONJUNCTIVAL HEMORRHAGE

Cause of Subconjunctival Hemorrhage
- _____
- _____
- _____
- _____
- _____
- _____

Notes

Signs and Symptoms of Subconjunctival Hemorrhage
- _____

Treatment of Subconjunctival Hemorrhage
- _____

SJOGREN'S SYNDROME

Cause of Sjogren's Syndrome
- _____

Signs and Symptoms of Sjogren's Syndrome
- _____
- _____
- _____

Treatment of Sjogren's Syndrome
- _____
- _____

BLEPHARITIS

Causes of Blepharitis
- _____

Signs and Symptoms of Blepharitis
- _____

Treatment of Blepharitis
- _____
- _____
- _____

Concerns of Blepharitis
- _____

Difference Between Healthy Eye and Blepharitis
- _____

Notes

ALLERGIC RHINITIS

Cause of Allergic Rhinitis
- _____
- _____

Signs and Symptoms of Allergic Rhinitis
- _____
- _____
- _____
- _____
- _____
- _____

Treatment of Allergic Rhinitis
- _____
- _____
- _____
- _____
- _____
- _____

Diagnostics of Allergic Rhinitis
- _____
- _____
- _____

Concerns of Allergic Rhinitis
- _____
- _____

EPISTAXIS

Introduction of Epistaxis
- _____

Cause of Epistaxis
- _____

Signs and Symptoms of Epistaxis
- _____
- _____
- _____

Notes

Treatment of Epistaxis
- _____
- _____

Concerns of Epistaxis
- _____

EARS

CHOLESTEATOMA

Definition of Cholesteatoma
- _____
_____

Cause of Cholesteatoma
- Keratinizing squamous epithelium _____

Signs and Symptoms of Cholesteatoma
- _____
- _____
- _____
- _____

Treatment of Cholesteatoma
- _____
- _____

CONDUCTIVE vs. SENSORINEURAL HEARING LOSS

Definition of Conductive vs. Sensorineural Hearing Loss
- _____
_____

Causes of Conductive vs. Sensorineural Hearing Loss
- _____
_____

Notes

Characteristic of Conductive vs. Sensorineural Hearing Loss
- Weber: _____
- Rinne: _____

Signs and Symptoms of Conductive vs. Sensorineural Hearing Loss
- Sensorineural Loss (impaired transmission of sound through the nervous system): _____
_____

ACUTE OTITIS MEDIA

Definition of Acute Otitis Media
- _____

Short Overview of Acute Otitis Media
- _____

Impact of Acute Otitis Media
- _____
- _____

Causes of Acute Otitis Media
- _____
- _____
- _____

Signs and Symptoms of Acute Otitis Media
- _____
- _____

Diagnostic of Acute Otitis Media
- Non-severe: _____
- Severe: _____

Treatment of Acute Otitis Media
- _____
- _____
- _____

Notes

Another Treatment of Acute Otitis Media
- _____
- _____

What Does Acute Otitis Media Look Like
- _____

Most Common Bacterial Causes
- _____
- _____
- _____

Concerns of Acute Otitis Media
- _____
- _____
- _____

OTITIS MEDIA WITH EFFUSION

Definition of Otitis Media With Effusion
- _____
  _____

Signs and Symptoms of Otitis Media With Effusion
- _____
  _____

Characteristic of Otitis Media With Effusion
- _____
- _____

Treatment of Otitis Media With Effusion
- _____
  _____
- _____
- _____

OTITIS EXTERNA

Definition of Otitis Externa
- _____
  _____

Notes

An Overview of Otitis Externa
- _____
  _____

Impact of Otitis Externa
- _____
- _____
- _____
- _____

Causes of Otitis Externa
- _____
- _____
- _____
- _____

Signs and Symptoms of Otitis Externa
- _____
- _____
- _____
- _____
- _____

Diagnostic of Otitis Externa
- _____

Treatment of Otitis Externa
- _____
  _____
- _____

Concerns of Otitis Externa
- _____

Medication Treatment of Otitis Externa
- _____

Notes

PRESBYCUSIS

Definition of Presbycusis
- _____
_____

Causes of Presbycusis
- Sensorineural loss without lateralization _____

Symptoms of Presbycusis
- _____
- _____
- _____

Common Age:
- _____

MENIERE'S DISEASE

Definition of Meniere's Disease
- _____
_____

Causes of Meniere's Disease
- Increased pressure within endolymphatic system
_____

Signs and Symptoms of Meniere's Disease
- _____
_____
- _____
_____

Diagnosis of Meniere's Disease
- _____
- _____
- _____
- _____
- _____

Notes

Treatment of Meniere's Disease

- _____
  _____
  _____

Concerns of Meniere's Disease

- _____
  _____

- _____

BATTLE SIGN

Cause of Battle Sign

- _____

Signs and Symptoms of Battle Sign

- _____
- _____

Diagnostics of Battle Sign

- _____

Treatment of Battle Sign

- _____
- _____

CLEAR GOLDEN FLUID DISCHARGE FROM NOSE/EAR

Causes of Clear Golden Fluid Discharge from Nose/Ear

- _____

Signs and Symptoms of Clear Golden Fluid Discharge from Nose/Ear

- _____

Treatment of Clear Golden Fluid Discharge from Nose/Ear

- _____

Diagnostics of Clear Golden Fluid Discharge from Nose/Ear

- Test fluid with urine dipstick - _____

```
Notes



```

THROAT

SIALOLITHIASIS

Definition of Sialolithiasis
- _____

An Overview of Sialolithiasis
- _____
  _____

Causes of Sialolithiasis
- _____

Common Area of Sialolithiasis
- _____

MEASLES (Koplik Spots)

How Does Measles Present
- _____

Signs & Symptoms of Measles (Koplik Spots)
- Accompanied by other ssx:
  - _____
  - _____
  - _____
  - _____

Cause of Measles
- _____

Treatment of Measles
- Tx: _____

ANTHRAX

Definition of Anthrax
- _____
  _____

Notes

Anthrax can be Caused by
- _____

Characteristic of Anthrax
- _____
  _____

Treatment of Anthrax
- _____
- _____
- _____

PERITONSILLAR ABSCESS

Signs and Symptoms of Peritonsillar Abscess
- _____
  _____
  _____

Treatment of Peritonsillar Abscess
- _____

Diagnostics of Peritonsillar Abscess
- _____
  _____
- _____
  _____

DIPHTHERIA

Signs and Symptoms of Diphtheria
- _____
- _____
- _____
- _____
- _____
- _____
- _____
- _____
- _____

Notes

Treatment of Diphtheria
- _____

Diagnostics of Diphtheria
- _____

EPIGLOTTITIS

Signs and Symptoms of Epiglottitis
- _____
- _____
- _____
- _____
- _____
- _____
- _____

Treatment of Epiglottitis
- _____

Concerns of Epiglottitis
- _____

PHARYNGITIS

Causes of Pharyngitis
- _____
- _____
- _____

Signs and Symptoms (viral) of Pharyngitis
- _____
- _____
- _____
- _____
- _____

Treatment of Pharyngitis
- _____

Notes

STREP THROAT

Causes of Strep Throat

- _____
- _____
- _____

Signs and Symptoms of Strep Throat

- _____
- _____
- _____
- _____
- _____
- _____
- _____

Diagnostic of Strep Throat

- _____
- _____
- _____
- _____
- _____
- _____
- _____
- _____
- _____

Treatment of Strep Throat

- _____
- _____
- _____
- _____
- _____
- _____
- _____

Concerns of Strep Throat

- _____
- _____
- _____

Notes

MONONUCLEOSIS

Causes of Mononucleosis
- EBV (incubation is 30-50 days) _____

Signs and Symptoms of Mononucleosis
- _____
- _____
- _____
- _____
- _____

Diagnostic of Mononucleosis
- CBC: _____
- LFT: _____
- Heterophile antibody test: _____
  _____

Treatment of Mononucleosis
- _____
- _____
- _____
- _____
- _____

Concerns of Mononucleosis
- _____
- _____
- _____

APHTHOUS ULCER/ STOMATITIS

Causes of Aphthous Ulcer/ Stomatitis
- _____

Signs and Symptoms of Aphthous Ulcer/ Stomatitis
- _____
- _____
- _____

Treatment of Aphthous Ulcer/ Stomatitis
- _____

Notes

GEOGRAPHIC TONGUE

Causes of Geographic Tongue
- _____

Signs and Symptoms of Geographic Tongue
- _____
- _____

LEUKOPLAKIA

Causes of Leukoplakia
- _____
- _____
- _____

Signs and Symptoms of Leukoplakia
- _____
- _____
- _____

Treatment of Leukoplakia
- _____
    *Self-Limiting

Notes

Notes

HEAD, EARS, EYES, NOSE, THROAT

HEMATOLOGY

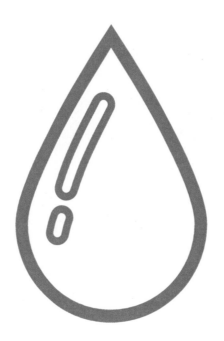

HEMATOLOGY

Definition of Hematology
- _____
  _____

Hematology Presents These Problems
- _____
- _____
- _____
- _____
- _____
- _____
- _____
- _____

ANEMIA

Definition of Anemia
- _____

What is the Function of RBC?
- _____

Types of Anemia
- _____
- _____
- _____
- _____
- _____
- _____
- _____
- _____
- _____
- _____

Notes

Symptoms of Anemia

- _____
- _____
- _____
- _____
- _____
- _____
- _____
- _____
- _____

Risk Factors of Anemia

- _____
- _____
- _____
- _____
- _____
- _____

Treatment of Anemia

- _____
- Treatment will depend on the type and cause of anemia
  - Iron deficiency anemia: _____
  - Vitamin deficiency anemias: _____
  - Thalassemia: _____
- Anemia of chronic disease: _____
  - Aplastic anemia: _____
  - Sickle cell anemia: _____
  - Hemolytic anemia: _____

Notes

Facts About Anemia

- _____
- _____
- _____
- _____

MICROCYTIC HYPOCHROMIC ANEMIA

Meaning of Anemia

- _____

What is Hypochromic?

- _____

When Microcytic Hypochromic Anemia Occurs?

- _____

List of Microcytic Hypochromic Anemia

- _____
- _____
- _____
- _____

Difference Between Microcytic Hypochromic Anemia and Normal Blood Smear

- _____

Check Ferritin

- _____

THALASSEMIA

What is Thalassemia?

- _____

What is Hemoglobin?

- _____

What is the Result When Occurs Thalassemia?

- _____

Notes

What Causes Low Hemoglobin Levels?
- When there isn't enough hemoglobin
    - _____
    - _____
  - _____

Difference Between Normal and Thalassemia
- Normal
    - _____
    - _____
    - _____
- Thalassemia
    - _____
    - _____
    - _____

What Does Hemoglobin Look Like?
  - _____

Types of Thalassemia
- There are two main types of thalassemia:
    - _____
        - _____
    - _____
        - _____
    - Note
      Only BETA THALASSEMIA will be abnormal with this—NOT alpha.
        - ALPHA-Asian
        - BETA-by sea

Diagnosis of Thalassemia
- Various blood tests are used to diagnose thalassemia:
    - _____
    - _____
    - _____
    - _____

Treatment of Thalassemia
- Treatments for moderate to severe thalassemia may include:
    - _____

NO IRON

Notes

HEMATOLOGY

IRON DEFICIENT- MICROCYTIC HYPOCHROMIC

Definition of Microcytic Anemia
- _____
  _____

Definition of Iron Deficiency
- _____

Causes of Iron Deficient-Microcytic Hypochromic
- _____
- _____

How Do You Treat Low Iron Levels?
- _____
- _____

HYPOCHROMIC MICROCYTIC ANEMIAS

- Definition of Hypochromic Microcytic Anemias
  - _____
- What Causes in Low Levels of Hemoglobin in Red Blood Cell?
  - _____
- What Causes In Microcytic Hypochromic Anemia?
  - _____

Symptoms of Iron Deficient-Microcytic Hypochromic
- _____
- _____
- _____
- _____
- _____
- _____
- _____

Severe and Prolonged Symptoms of Iron Deficient-Microcytic Hypochromic
- _____
- _____
- _____
- _____
- Plummer-Vinson Syndrome: _____
- _____
- _____

Notes

Diagnosis of Iron Deficient-Microcytic Hypochromic
- _____
- _____
- _____

Treatment of Iron Deficient-Microcytic Hypochromic
- _____
- _____
- Caution: _____

MACROCYTIC ANEMIA

What is Macrocytic Anemia?
- _____

Why Use Femtoliters?
- _____

Diagnosis of Macrocytic Anemia
- _____

Causes of Macrocytic Anemia
- _____
- _____
- _____

B12:
- _____

PERNICIOUS ANEMIA

What is Pernicious Anemia
- _____
- _____

Vitamin B12
- _____

Notes

HEMATOLOGY

What Are Essential Nutrients Discuss Their Importance In Our Body?
- _____
  _____

Diagnosis of Pernicious Anemia
- B12 foods: _____
- _____

Treatment of Pernicious Anemia
- PERNICIOUS: _____

FOLATE-DEFICIENCY ANEMIA

What is Folate-Deficiency Anemia
- _____
  _____

Another Name of Folate-Deficiency Anemia
- _____

An Overview of Folate-Deficiency Anemia
- _____

Causes of Folate-Deficiency Anemia
- _____
- _____
- _____
- _____

Does Not Cause
- _____

Symptoms of Folate-Deficiency Anemia
- _____
- _____
- _____
- _____
- _____
- _____

Notes

Treatment and Management of Folate-Deficiency Anemia
- _____
- _____
- _____

SICKLE CELL ANEMIA

Definition of Sickle Cell Anemia
- _____
  _____

A Short Overview of Sickle Cell Anemia
- _____
  _____

Symptoms of Sickle Cell Anemia
- _____
- _____
- _____
- _____
- _____

Complications of Sickle Cell Anemia
- _____
- _____
- _____
- _____

Diagnosis of Sickle Cell Anemia
- _____
- _____
- _____

Treatment of Sickle Cell Anemia
- _____
- _____
- _____
- Give sickle cell patients their vaccines to protect from illnesses such as:
  - _____
    OR
  - _____

Notes

HODGKIN LYMPHOMA

Definition of Hodgkin Lymphoma

- _____
  _____

A Short Overview of Hodgkin Lymphoma

Stage IIE Adult of Hodgkin Lymphoma

- _____

Symptoms of Hodgkin Lymphoma

- _____
- _____
- _____
- _____
- _____
- _____

Treatment of Hodgkin Lymphoma

- _____
- _____

IDIOPATHIC THROMBOCYTOPENIC PURPURA (ITP)

Definition of Idiopathic Thrombocytopenic Purpura (ITP)

- _____
  _____

What are Platelets?

- _____

What Does ITP Look Like?

- _____

Notes

Forms of Idiopathic Thrombocytopenic Purpura (ITP)

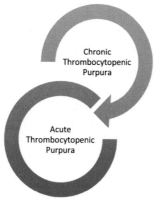

Causes of Idiopathic Thrombocytopenic Purpura (ITP)
- _____

Symptoms of Idiopathic Thrombocytopenic Purpura (ITP)
- _____
- _____
- _____
- _____
- _____

Diagnosis of Idiopathic Thrombocytopenic Purpura (ITP)
- _____
- _____
- _____

Treatment of Idiopathic Thrombocytopenic Purpura (ITP)
- _____
- _____

Avoid These Medicines!!
- _____
- _____
- _____
- _____

Notes

THROMBOSIS

Definition of Thrombosis
- _____
  _____

Types of Thrombosis
- _____ thrombosis
- _____ thrombosis

By Graphical Presentation
Problems Caused by Thrombosis
- A superficial thrombus can cause
  - _____
  - _____
  - _____

Risk Factors of Thrombosis
- _____
- _____
- _____
- _____

Diagnosis of Thrombosis
- _____
- _____
- _____

Treatment of Thrombosis
- _____
  or
- _____
  or
- _____

Prevention of Thrombosis
- _____
- _____
- _____
- _____
- _____

Notes

HEMATOLOGY

Notes

HEMATOLOGY

MEN & WOMEN'S HEALTH WITH STIS

MEN'S HEALTH REVIEW

Facts About Men's Health
- Top Causes of Death:
    - _____
    - _____
    - _____
- Men are nearly _____ as likely as women to die prematurely from diabetes
- The peak age for male suicide is _____

ACUTE BACTERIAL PROSTATITIS

Definition of Acute Bacterial Prostatitis
- _____
  _____

What Type Of Bacteria Causes Prostatitis?
- _____

Signs and Symptoms of Acute Bacterial Prostatitis
- _____
- _____
- _____
- _____
- _____
- _____
- _____

Treatment of Acute Bacterial Prostatitis
- Older than 35:
    - _____
    - _____
    - Other: _____
- Younger than 35:
    - _____
    - _____

Diagnosis of Acute Bacterial Prostatitis
- _____
- _____

Notes

TESTICULAR TORSION

Definition of Testicular Torsion
- _____
  _____

Signs of Testicular Torsion
- _____
- _____
- _____
- _____

How Common is Testicular Torsion?
- _____
- _____
- _____

Difference Between Normal and Testicular Torsion Testicle
- _____

Treatment/ Management
- _____
  _____

ERECTILE DYSFUNCTION

Definition of Erectile Dysfunction
- _____
  _____

How Common is Erectile Dysfunction?
- _____
- _____

Causes of:
- _____
- _____
- _____

Caused by:
- _____
- _____
- _____
- _____

Notes
_____

Treatment Option for Erectile Dysfunction
- Therapy stage
  - First line:
    - Treatment option
      a. _____
      b. _____
  - Second line:
    - Treatment option
      1. _____
      2. _____
      3. _____
  - Third line:
      1. _____

BALANITIS

Definition of Balanitis
- _____
  _____

Common Area of Balanitis
- _____

How Common is Balanitis
- _____
- _____

Causes for
- _____
- _____
- _____
- _____

Difference Between Normal and Balanitis Affected Penis
- _____

Symptoms of Balanitis
- _____
- _____
- _____
- _____
- _____

Notes

Precautions and Treatment of Balanitis
- Discontinue the use:
  - _____
- Use only:
  - _____

Medications of Balanitis
- _____

WOMAN'S HEALTH REVIEW

Facts About Women's Health
- _____
- _____
- _____

Natural Estrogen
- Estrogen level can be increased by:
  - _____
  - _____
  - _____

ECTOPIC PREGNANCY

Definition of Ectopic Pregnancy
- _____
  _____

Causes of Ectopic Pregnancy
- _____

Risk Factors of Ectopic Pregnancy
- _____
- _____
- _____
- _____

Notes

Symptoms of Ectopic Pregnancy
- _____
- _____
- _____
- _____

Difference between Normal and Ectopic Pregnancy
- _____

Diagnosis and Treatment
- _____
- _____
- _____
- _____

OVARIAN CANCER

Definition of Ovarian Cancer
- _____
  _____

Most Common Age of Ovarian Cancer
- _____

Signs of Stage 1 Ovarian Cancer
- _____
- _____

Main Cause of Ovarian Cancer
- **Risk-**_____

Treatment of Ovarian Cancer
- _____
- _____

Difference Between Normal Ovary and Ovary with Cancer
- _____

Responsible for Ovarian Cancer
- _____

Notes

Risks of Ovarian Cancer
- _____
- _____
- _____
- _____
- _____

CA 125 Gene:
- _____

BREAST CANCER

Definition of Breast Cancer
- _____
  _____

Breast Cancer Detected By
- _____
- _____

Difference Between Mass vs Cyst
- _____

Diagnosis of Breast Cancer
- _____

What is a Pap Smear?
- _____

Steps of Cypore Pap Smear Test
Increased opportunity to detect early signs of abnormality, Addressing 2/3 of false negative due to sampling and preparations errors):
- _____
- _____
- _____
- _____
- _____

LOW-GRADE SQUAMOUS INTRAEPITHELIAL LESION (LSIL)

Definition of Low-Grade Squamous Intraepithelial Lesion (LSIL)
- _____
  _____

Notes

LSIL Caused by

- _____

Treatment of LSIL

- _____

LSIL Recommendation Includes
- 21-24 years old: _____
- 25-29 years old: _____

Diagnosis of LSIL

- _____
- _____

HIGH-GRADE SQUAMOUS INTRAEPITHELIAL LESION (HSIL)

Definition of High-Grade Squamous Intraepithelial Lesion (HSIL)

- _____
  _____

How Serious is HSIL?

- _____

What Causes HSIL?

- _____

HSIL Recommendation Includes
- 21-24 years old: _____
- >25 years old: _____

Cervical Changes
- By graphical presentation

    - _____
    - _____
    - _____
    - _____

BACTERIAL VAGINOSIS

Definition of Bacterial Vaginosis

- _____
  _____

Notes

An Overview of Bacterial Vaginosis
- _____
- _____

What is Whiff Test?
- _____
  _____

A Strong Fishy Odor
- _____

What Does Bacterial Vaginosis Look Like?
- _____

Symptoms of Bacterial Vaginosis
- _____
- _____
- _____
- _____

Risk of Bacterial Vaginosis
- _____
- _____
- _____
- _____
- _____
- _____

Diagnosis of Bacterial Vaginosis
- _____
- _____
- _____

Difference Between Healthy Vaginal Mucosa and Bacterial Vaginosis
- _____

Treatment of Bacterial Vaginosis
- _____

**Treating the partner is not necessary

CANDIDAL VAGINITIS

Definition of Candidal Vaginitis
- _____
  _____

Notes

A Short Overview of Candidal Vaginitis
- _____
  _____

Diagnosis of Candidal Vaginitis
- _____

What Does It Look It?
- _____

Symptoms of Candidal Vaginitis
- _____
- _____
- _____
- _____

Treatment of Candidal Vaginitis
- _____
- _____

VAGINAL ATROPHY

Definition of Vaginal Atrophy
- _____
  _____

Vaginal Atrophy Occur
- _____

Causes for Vaginal Atrophy
- _____

Treatment of Vaginal Atrophy
- _____

Difference Between Healthy Vagina and Vaginal Atrophy
- _____

Notes

POSTMENOPAUSAL BLEEDING

Definition of Postmenopausal Bleeding
- _____
  _____

Diagnosis or Test of Postmenopausal Bleeding
- _____
- _____

What is the Percentage Of Postmenopausal Bleeding That Is Cancer?
- _____
- _____

GALACTORRHEA

Definition of Galactorrhea
- _____
  _____

Cause
- _____
- _____

Diagnosis of Galactorrhea
- Labs: _____
- Dx: _____

Treatment of Galactorrhea
- Meds: _____

SEXUALLY TRANSMITTED INFECTION

SEXUALLY TRANSMITTED INFECTIONS

What is a Sexually Transmitted Infection
- _____
  _____

Meaning of Sensitivity (+)
- _____
- i.e. _____
- Ex. _____

Notes

Meaning of Specificity (-)

- _____
  - i.e. _____
  - Ex. _____

Gold Standard

- _____

Difference Between Sensitivity and Specificity

- Sensitivity
  - Definition
    - _____
  - 100% (1.0) means
    - _____
  - Statistical outcome
    - _____
  - Ideal test result
    - _____
  - Test interpretation
    - _____
    - _____
  - The rule
    - _____
- Specificity
  - Definition
    - _____
  - 100% (1.0) means
    - _____
  - Statistical outcome
    - _____
  - Ideal test result
    - _____
  - Test interpretation
    - _____
    - _____
  - The rule
    - _____

Notes

CHLAMYDIA

Definition of Chlamydia
- _____
  _____

Most Common
- _____

A Short Overview of Chlamydia
- Organism: _____
- Recommendation: _____
- Partners should be: _____

**Report to the health department

Complications of Chlamydia
- _____
- _____
- _____
- _____
- _____

Fitz Hugh Curtis Syndrome Symptoms
- _____
- _____
- _____
- _____
- _____
- _____
- _____

Who Carry the Highest Incidence of Disease?
- _____

Predominantly asymptomatic
- Men
  - _____
- Women
  - _____

Symptoms of Chlamydia
- Chlamydia symptoms in men
  - _____
  - _____
- Chlamydia symptoms in women
  - _____
  - _____
  - _____

Notes

Diagnosis of Chlamydia
- _____

Treatment of Chlamydia
- Single dose: _____
  or
- _____

Definition of Gonorrhea
- _____
  _____

Organism
- _____

Incidence
- _____

Leads to
- _____
- _____

Predominantly Asymptomatic
- Dysuria _____
- Yellow-green discharge _____

Common Symptoms of Gonorrhea
- Men
  - _____
  - _____
  - _____
- Women
  - _____
  - _____
  - _____

Notes

Untreated Gonorrhea Can Lead to What Serious Problems

- _____
- _____
- _____
- _____

Treatment of Gonorrhea

- _____
- _____
- _____

SYPHILIS

Definition of Syphilis

- _____
  _____

Incidence

- _____

Organism:

- _____

Sign of Syphilis Stage 1

- _____

*REPORTABLE

Screening

- _____
- _____

Stages of Syphilis

- _____
- _____
- _____
- _____

What Does It Look Like?

- _____

Treatment of Syphilis

- _____
- Penicillin allergy: _____

**Report to the health department

Notes

HPV (CONDYLOMA ACUMINATA)

Definition of HPV (Condyloma Acuminata)
- _____

A Short Overview of HPV(Condyloma Acuminata)
- _____

What Does It Look Like?
- _____

HPV (Condyloma Acuminata) Caused by
- _____

Diagnosis of HPV (Condyloma Acuminata)
- _____

Treatment of HPV (Condyloma Acuminata)
- _____

Vaccine of HPV (Condyloma Acuminata)
- _____
- _____

EPIDIDYMITIS

Definition of Epididymitis
- _____

Most Common Causative
- _____

Suspected
- _____

(+) Prehn's sign
- _____

Notes

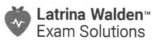

What Does an Epididymitis Testicle Look Like?
- _____

Difference between Healthy Testicle and Epididymis Affected Testicle
- _____

Symptoms of Epididymitis
- _____
- _____
- _____
- _____
- _____
- _____

Diagnosis of Epididymitis
- _____

Treatment of Epididymitis
- _____
- _____

PELVIC INFLAMMATORY DISEASE

Definition of Pelvic Inflammatory Disease
- _____
  _____

Common Causes of Pelvic Inflammatory Disease
- _____
- _____

Delay in Treatment May Lead To
- _____
- _____
- _____

Lab Test
- _____

Difference between Healthy female Reproductive System and Reproductive System with PID
- _____

A Short Overview of Pelvic Inflammatory Disease
- _____
  - _____

Notes

Symptoms of Pelvic Inflammatory Disease
- Major criteria
    - _____
    - _____
    - _____
    - _____
- Rx(treatment)
    - _____
    - _____
- Supporting criteria
    - _____
    - _____
    - _____
    - _____
    - _____
- Chandeliar Sign
    - _____

What is Salpingitis?
- _____

Salpingitis is Caused By
- _____

Treatment of Pelvic Inflammatory Disease
- _____

TRICHOMONAS VAGINALIS

Definition of Trichomonas Vaginalis
- _____
  _____

TV Can Infect
- _____
- _____
- _____

TV is Caused By
- _____

Notes

Diagnosis of TV
- _____

Asymptomatic in Men
- _____
- _____
- _____
- _____

Symptoms of TV
- _____
- _____
- _____
- _____

Wet Prep (Wet Mount)
- Left side
  - _____
  - _____
  - _____
- Right side
  - _____
  - _____
  - _____

Treatment of TV
- _____
  - or
- _____

Symptoms of This Treatment
- _____
- _____
- _____
- _____

Notes

Notes

MUSCULOSKELETAL

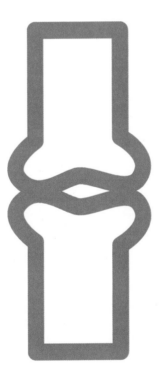

TENDON RUPTURE

Definition of Biceps Tendon Rupture
- _____
  _____

Causes of Biceps Tendon Rupture
- Two main causes of biceps tendon tears:
  - _____
  - _____

Hook Test
- _____
- _____
- _____
- _____

ROTATOR CUFF DESCRIPTION

Definition of Rotator Cuff
- _____
  _____

Rotator Cuff injury
- _____
- _____

The four Rotator Cuff muscles
- _____
- _____
- _____
- _____

Apprehension Test
This test checks for a possible torn labrum or anterior instability problem
- The examiner stands either _____ or at the _____, grasps the _____ with one hand, and passively _____ the humerus to end range with the shoulder in _____ of abduction
- _____ pressure is then applied to the _____ aspect of the humeral head by the _____ or the _____ (if the patient is in supine).
- A _____ for anterior instability is if apprehension is presented by the patient or if the patient reports pain
- Positive means pain is _____ on relocation test and positive use. Rotator cuff injury: disturbed sleep, arm weakness, dull ache

Notes

NAVICULAR FRACTURE

Definition of Navicular Fracture
- _____
  _____

Cause of Navicular Fracture
- _____

Symptoms
- _____

KNEES

Anterolateral aspect of right knee
- Seen from an angle between anteriorly and laterally
  - _____
  - _____
  - _____
  - _____
  - _____
  - _____
  - _____
  - _____
  - _____
  - _____
  - _____
  - _____
  - _____
  - _____

Notes

DRAWER TEST

What is the Drawer Test?
- _____
  _____

How do you perform the Drawer Test?
- _____
  _____

The Drawer Test Is Used for:
- _____

Types of Drawer Test:
- _____
- _____

LACHMAN TEST

What is Lachman Test?
- _____
  _____

How do you perform the Lachman test?
- _____
  _____

MCMURRAY TEST

Definition of McMurray Test
- _____
  _____

Components of McMurray Test
- There are 2 components
  - _____
  - _____

Notes

- How do you perform the McMurray Test?
  - When assessing the _____, the stress applied is a _____ force with passive _____ rotation and extension of the _____
  - A popping or clicking sound is a _____ finding for a lateral meniscus injury
  - Starting with the patient's _____ and _____ fully flexed, apply a _____ while passively internally rotating the _____ and extending the _____ simultaneously

JOINT HEALTH

Joint and Phalanges

- _____
- _____
- _____
- _____
- _____

OSTEOARTHRITIS (OA)

Definition of Osteoarthritis (OA)

- _____

Osteoarthritis (OA) Most Commonly Found

- _____

Sign of Osteoarthritis (OA)

- _____
- _____

Exercise and Precautions

- Isometric exercises for knee OA
  - _____
- Non-weight bearing, like: _____

Notes

Treatment
- First-line medication
  - _____
- Lifestyle
- Low impact exercise
  - _____
  - _____
  - _____
- Knee braces
  - _____
- Corticosteroids injections or topical

OSTEOPOROSIS

Definition of Osteoporosis
- _____
  _____

Best Weight-Bearing:
- _____
- _____
- Difference between Healthy and Osteoporosis Bone
  - _____

Medication
Bisphosphonates "onate": FOSAMAX (alendronate sodium)
- IMPORTANT INSTRUCTIONS
  - _____
  - _____
  - _____
  - _____
  - _____

- Calcium and Vitamin Requirement:
  - According to Notional Academy of Medicine (Formerly Institute of Medicine)
    - Vitamin D
      - Age 19-70: _____
      - Age<70: _____
    - Calcium:
      - Women
        - Age 19-50: _____
        - Age<50: _____
      - Men
        - Age 19-70: _____
        - Age<70: _____

Notes

RHEUMATOID ARTHRITIS (RA)

What is Rheumatoid Arthritis (RA)
- _____
  _____

Signs of Rheumatoid Arthritis (RA)
- _____
- _____
- _____
- _____

Treatment
- _____
- _____
- _____
- _____

MEDIAL TIBIAL STRESS SYNDROME OF FRACTURE

Definition of Medial Tibial Stress Syndrome of Fracture
- _____
  _____

Injuries occur
- _____

Signs of Medial Tibial Stress Syndrome of Fracture
- _____

Treatment of Medial Tibial Stress Syndrome of Fracture
- _____
- _____

Notes

MUSCULOSKELETAL

LATERAL EPICONDYLITIS

Definition of Lateral Epicondylitis
- _____
_____

Common area of Injury
- _____
_____

Signs of Lateral Epicondylitis
- _____
- _____

Treatment
- _____
- _____

MEDIAL EPICONDYLITIS (GOLFER'S ELBOW)

Definition of Medial Epicondylitis (Golfer's Elbow)
- _____
_____

Others Name of Medial Epicondylitis (Golfer's Elbow)
- _____
- _____
- _____
- _____

Treatment
- _____
- _____

Notes

MORTON'S NEUROMA

Definition of Morton's Neuroma
- _____
  _____

Most Common Area
- _____

Diagnosis of Morton's Neuroma
- _____

Signs of Morton's Neuroma
- _____
- _____
- _____

Treatment
- Refer

Mulder Test
- When assessing the _____, the stress applied is a _____ force with _____ rotation and extension of the_____.
- A _____ occurs when the patient feels the _____ in the _____(or plantar) surface of their _____.
- The pain the patient feels with the test may spread to _____ and sometimes a click (Mulder's click) can also be heard.
- The presence of a _____ does not indicate a positive Mulder's sign; the pain must be _____ to have a positive Mulder's sign.

SCOLIOSIS

Definition of Scoliosis
- _____
  _____

Most Common Region
- _____
- _____

Notes

MUSCULOSKELETAL

Adams Forward Bend Test
- The patient needs to bend _____, starting at the _____ until the _____ comes in the horizontal plane, with the _____ together, _____ hanging and the knees in _____

- Both arms hanging freely, _____ straight, look for _____ of spine, scapular, thoracic, lumbar curvature; inspect _____ and _____ for asymmetry

LOW BACK PAIN

Definition of Low Back Pain:
- Low back pain is a universal human experience; almost everyone has it at some point
  - Lumbar Region:
    - _____
  - Diagnosis
    - _____
  - Common causes
    - _____
  - Aggravated by
    - _____
  - Relieved by
    - _____

Lumbar stenosis
- Aggravated by
  - _____
  - _____
- Relieved by
  - _____
  - _____

POLYMYALGIA RHEUMATICA

Definition of Polymyalgia Rheumatica
- _____
  _____

An overview of Polymyalgia Rheumatica
- How long does it last:
  - _____

Notes

Treatment of Polymyalgia Rheumatica
- _____
- _____

ANKYLOSING SPONDYLITIS

Definition of Ankylosing Spondylitis
- _____
  _____

Sings of Ankylosing Spondylitis
- _____
  _____

Treatment
- _____
- _____
- _____

Difference of Normal, Early and Advanced Spine
- _____

Notes

Notes

MUSCULOSKELETAL

NEUROLOGY

NEUROLOGY

Definition of Neurology

- _____
  _____

  _____

CRANIAL NERVES

Definition of Cranial Nerves

- _____
  _____

An overview of Cranial Nerves - what are the 12 Cranial Nerves?

1. _____
2. _____
3. _____
4. _____
5. _____
6. _____
7. _____
8. _____
9. _____
10. _____
11. _____
12. _____

Notes

CN I- NOSE OLFACTORY NERVE

Definition

- _____
  _____

Consequences of Disruption of Olfactory Nerve

- _____
- _____
- _____

Anatomy of Olfactory Nerve

- _____
- _____
- _____
- _____
- _____
- _____
- _____
- _____

THE OPTIC NERVE

Definition

- _____
  _____

What Does the Optic Nerve Look Like?

- _____
  _____

THE OCULOMOTOR NERVE

Definition

- _____
  _____

Notes
_____
_____
_____
_____
_____
_____

What Are the Two Different Motor Functions of Oculomotor Nerve?
- Muscle function
  - _____
- Pupil response
  - _____

Position of Oculomotor Nerve Anatomy of Oculomotor Nerve
- _____
- _____
- _____
- _____
- _____
- _____
- _____
- _____
- Midbrain
  - _____

THE TROCHLEAR NERVE

Definition of Trochlear Nerve
- _____
  _____

Cause of Diplopia and How Can it be Improved?
- _____

THE TRIGEMINAL NERVE

Definition of Trigeminal Nerve
- _____
  _____

Where Does the Trigeminal Nerve Originate?
- _____

How Do You Separate Sensory Root and Motor Root Form?
- _____

Notes

Three Division of Trigeminal Nerve
- Ophthalmic
  - _____
    _____

- Maxillary
  - _____
    _____

- Mandibular
  - _____
    _____

THE ABDUCENS NERVE

Definition of Abducens Nerve
- _____
  _____

Function of Lateral Rectus Muscle
- _____
  - For example, you would use it to look: _____
  - Why is the Abducens Nerve also called Abducent Nerve?
    - _____

THE FACIAL NERVE

Definition of Facial nerve
- _____
  _____

An Overview of Facial nerve

Where is the Facial Nerve located in the brain?
- _____

How Does the Facial Nerve form?
- _____

What Does it Look Like?
- _____

Notes
_____

THE VESTIBULOCOCHLEAR NERVE

Definition of Vestibulocochlear Nerve
- _____
  _____

Components of Vestibulocochlear Nerve
- The cochlear component
  - _____
- The vestibular portion
  - _____

Origination of Vestibulocochlear Nerve?

The Vestibulocochlear nerve has two roots:
- _____
- _____

Cochlea
The fibers of the cochlear nerve arise from the central processes of _____, which are located in the _____ cells located in the _____.

THE GLOSSOPHARYNGEAL NERVE

Definition

- _____
  _____

Branches and Functions of Glossophayngeal nerve

- _____
- _____
- _____
- _____
- _____
- _____
- _____
- _____
- _____

Notes

NEUROLOGY

THE VAGUS NERVE

Definition of Vagus Nerve and What Does it Do?
- _____
  _____

Graphical Presentation of Vagus Nerve Stimulation (VNS)
- _____
- _____
- _____
- _____

THE SPINAL ACCESSORY NERVE

Definition
- _____
  _____

What Does it do?
- _____
  _____

What Does it Look Like?
- _____
  _____

THE HYPOGLOSSAL NERVE

Definition
- _____
  _____

Consequences of damaged hypoglossal nerve Physiology of hypoglossal nerve stimulation
- _____
- _____
- _____
- _____
- _____
- _____
- Intrinsic muscles of tongue:
    - _____
    - _____
    - _____

Notes

NEUROLOGICAL DISORDER

Definition

- _____
  _____

Common Neurological Disorders

- _____
- _____
- _____
- _____
- _____
- _____

MIGRAINE

Definition

- _____
  _____

How Does a Migraine Feel?

- _____
- _____

How Long is Too Long For a Migraine?

- _____
- _____
- _____

Symptoms

- _____
- _____
- _____
- _____
- _____
- _____
- _____

Notes

CLUSTER HEADACHES

Definition
- _____
  _____

Types of Headaches
- Sinus
  - _____
- Cluster
  - _____
- Tension
  - _____
- Migraine
  - _____

Occurrence of Cluster Headaches
- _____
- _____
- _____

Symptoms
- _____
- _____
- _____
- _____
- _____
- _____
- _____
- _____

Treatment
- _____
- _____

Notes

ESSENTIAL TREMOR

Definition
- _____
  _____

Symptoms
- _____
- _____
- _____
- _____
- _____
- _____
- _____

BENIGN PAROXYSMAL POSITIONAL VERTIGO

Definition
- _____
  _____

Symptoms
- _____
- _____
- _____
- _____
- _____
- Dix Hallpike test (Dix Hallpike Maneuver)
  - _____
  - _____

Treatment
- _____
OR
- _____

Notes

FIBROMYALGIA

Definition

- _____
  _____

How Does a Fibromyalgia feel?

- _____
  _____

How Long Does the Pain Exist?

- _____
- _____
- _____
- _____

SUBARACHNOID HEMORRHAGE

Definition

- _____
  _____

Causes of Subarachnoid Hemorrhage

- _____
  _____

Symptoms

- _____
- _____
- _____
- _____
- _____
- _____
- _____
- _____
- _____
- _____

Treatment

- _____
- _____
- _____

Notes

SUBDURAL HEMORRAGE

Definition of Subdural Hemorrhage

- _____
  _____

Why is Subdural Hemorrhage Life-Threatening??

- _____
- _____
- _____

Symptoms of Subdural Hemorrhage

- _____
- _____
- _____
- _____
- _____
- _____
- _____
- _____
- _____

Treatment of Subdural Hemorrhage

- _____
- _____

TRIGEMINAL NEURALGIA

Definition

- _____
  _____

What is the main cause of Trigeminal Neuralgia?

- _____
- _____
- _____

How does a Trigeminal Neuralgia feel?

- _____
- _____

Notes

Symptoms of Trigeminal Neuralgia
- The Main Symptoms
  - _____
  - _____

That Lasts From a Few Seconds to About Two Minutes
- Can be triggered by certain actions or movements:
  - _____
  - _____
  - _____
  - _____
  - _____

Treatment of Trigeminal Neuralgia
- _____

POLYMYALGIA RHEUMATICA

Definition of Polymyalgia Rheumatic
- _____
_____

Symptoms of Polymyalgia Rheumatica
- _____
- _____
- _____
- _____
- _____
- _____
- _____
- _____
- _____
- _____

TEMPORAL ARTERITIS

Definition of Temporal Arteritis
- _____
_____

Notes

Symptoms

- _____
- _____
- _____
- _____
- _____

Diagnosis and Examination

- _____
- _____
- _____
- Oral Prednisone 40-60mg
    - ○ _____
    - ○ _____

CARPAL TUNNEL SYNDROME

Definition of Carpal Tunnel Syndrome

- _____
  _____

Overview of Carpal Tunnel Syndrome

- _____
- Tinel's sign: _____
- Phalen's sign: _____
- _____

ABSENCE SEIZURE

Definition

- _____
  _____

Symptoms

- _____
- _____
- _____

Notes

How Does Seizure Threshold Decrease?

- _____

ALZHEIMER'S DISEASE

An Overview of Alzheimer's Disease

- _____
  _____

Definition of Alzheimer's Disease

- _____
  _____

Definition of Dementia

- _____
  _____

Causes of Dementia

- _____
- _____
- _____
- _____
- _____

LEWY BODY DEMENTIA

Definition

- _____
  _____

Causes of Lewy Body Dementia

- _____

Symptoms of Lewy Body Dementia

- _____
- _____

Notes

VASULAR DEMENTIA

Define

- _____
  _____

Ischemic Changes Due To

- _____
- _____
- _____

Symptoms

- _____
- _____
- _____
- _____

Mini-Mental State Examination (MMSE)

- _____
  _____
- _____
- _____

SYNCOPE

Definition

- _____

Causes

- _____

Types

- _____
- _____
- _____
- _____

Notes

NEUROLOGY

TENSION HEADACHES

Definition
- _____
  _____
  _____
  _____

Causes
- _____
- _____
- _____
- _____
- _____

4 Step Tension Headache Process
- _____
  _____
- _____
  _____
- _____
  _____
- _____
  _____

MENINGITIS

Definition
- _____
  _____
  _____

Most Common Causes:
- _____

Other Causes
- _____
- _____
- _____
- _____

Notes

Organisms That Cause Meningitis

- _____
- _____
- _____
- _____

Symptoms of Meningitis

- Central
  - _____
  - _____
- Ears
  - _____
- Eyes
  - _____
- Neck
  - _____
- Systemic
  - _____
- Trunk, mucus, membranes extremities (if meningococcal infection)
  - _____
- Exam For Meningitis
  - _____
  - _____

STROKE

Definition

- _____

What Happens During a Stroke?

- _____
  _____
  _____

Notes

Stroke
- _____

Heart Attack
- _____

_____

TRANSIENT ISCHEMIC ATTACK (TIA)

Definition
- _____
_____

TIA Are Often Called
- _____

About _____ people who have a TIA go on to have _____.

_____

BELL'S PALSY

Definition
- _____
_____
_____

EPILEPSY

Definition
- _____

Seizure
- _____
- _____

Affects
- _____

Notes

PARKINSON'S DISEASE

Definition

- _____
  _____
  _____
  _____

Symptoms

- _____
- _____
- _____
- _____

MULTIPLE SCLEROSIS

Definition

- _____
  _____
  _____
  _____
  _____
  _____

DELIRIUM

Definition

- _____
  _____

Sometimes Called

- _____
- _____
- _____

Notes

NEUROLOGY

Common Causes

- _____
- _____
- _____

NEUROFIBROMATOSIS

Definition

- _____
  _____

There are Two Major Types

- _____
- _____

Notes

Notes

NEUROLOGY

PEDIATRICS

5th DISEASE - Erythema Infectiosum

Condition

- _____
- Infection
  - _____
  - _____
  - Also
    - _____
    - _____
    - _____
- GI Symptoms
  - _____
  - _____
- Joints pain
  - _____
  - _____
  - _____
- Anemia - _____

Cause

- Parvovirus B19 _____

Diagnosis of 5th Disease

- _____
  - Presentation = _____

Treatment of 5th Disease

- Self-limiting – _____
- Use _____ for controlling (symptomatic control)
  - _____
  - _____
  - _____

Management and Education

- _____
- _____
- _____
- _____
- _____
- _____

Notes

ADHD

Condition

- _____
- _____
- _____
- _____
- _____

Diagnosis of ADHD

- Information gathering based _____
- Interviews and questionnaires for
    - _____
    - _____
    - _____
    - _____
    - _____
- _____
- _____

Causes of ADHD

- _____
- _____

Treatment of ADHD

1. _____
2. _____
3. _____
4. _____

Management and Education

- Behavior therapy **(should be _____)**
    - _____
- _____
- _____

Notes

PEDIATRICS

- Parenting skills training
  - _____
- Psychotherapy
  - _____
- Family therapy
  - _____

AUTISM

Characteristics

- _____
- _____
- _____
- _____
- _____
- _____
- _____
- _____
- _____

Diagnosis of Autism

- _____
- _____
- _____
- _____
- _____
- _____
- _____
- Developmental questionnaires, such as
  - _____

Management

- _____ therapy
- _____ therapy
- _____ therapy
- _____ therapy

Recommendation

- _____

Alternative Therapy

- _____
- _____

Notes

BRONCHIOLITIS

Mainly Affects

- _____

Causes of Bronchiolitis

- _____
- _____
- _____

Risk Factors

- AVOID fumes from chemical:
    - _____
    - _____
    - _____
    - _____
- _____
- _____

Signs and Symptoms

- _____
- _____
- Common cold, such as a
    - _____
    - _____
    - _____

Diagnosis

- _____

Treatment

1. _____
2. _____
3. _____
4. _____
5. _____

Management

- _____
- _____
- _____

Notes

PEDIATRICS

Recommendations
- _____
- _____
- _____

What Therapy Should Not Be Used For
- Bronchodilators
    - _____
    - _____
- _____
- _____
- _____

CAPUT SUCCEDANEUM

Look for…
- _____
- _____
- _____

Causes of Caput Succedaneum
- _____

Diagnosis
- _____
- _____

Will It Cross The Midline?
- _____

Treatment and Management of Caput Succedaneum
- _____
- If your child develops _____
    - _____
- _____

CEPHALOHEMATOMA

Define Cephalohematoma
- _____
- _____

Notes

Causes of Cephalohematoma

- _____

Diagnosis of Cephalohematoma

- _____
- _____
- _____
- _____
- _____

Will it Cross the Midline?

- _____

Treatment and Management of Cephalohematoma

- _____

CLOSING OF FONTANEL

- _____
- _____
- _____
- _____

COARCTATION OF AORTA

Define
- Narrowing of the aorta
    - _____
    - _____

Causes of Coarctation of Aorta

- _____
- _____

Diagnosis of Coarctation of Aorta

- _____
- _____

Notes

Additional Diagnostic Methods
- _____
- _____
- _____
- _____
- _____
- _____

Treatment of Coarctation of Aorta
- _____

Management and Patient Education
- _____
- _____
- _____

CROUP

Disease Concerns
- _____
- _____
- _____
- _____
- _____
- _____
- _____
- _____
- _____

Causes of Croup
- Main: _____
- Minor: _____
- _____
- _____

Notes

Diagnosis With Signs And Symptoms

- _____
- _____
- _____
- Examine the throat: _____
- _____
- Severe: _____
- _____

1St line Medication

- _____
- _____

Management and Education

- _____
- _____
- _____
- _____
- _____
- _____
- _____
- _____
- _____
- _____

CYANOSIS

Presentation of Cyanosis
- Bluish color
  - _____
  - _____
  - _____
- _____
- _____

Causes of Cyanosis
- _____
- _____
- _____

Notes

- _____
- _____
- _____
- _____
- _____

Diagnosis of Cyanosis

- _____
- _____
- _____
- _____
- _____
- _____
- _____
- _____
- _____

Treatment and Management

- _____
- _____
- _____
- _____
- _____
- _____

ENCOPRESIS

Concerns

- _____
- _____
- _____

Causes of Encopresis

- _____
- _____
- _____
- _____

Notes

- 4 types of children:
  - ○ _____
  - ○ _____
  - ○ _____
  - ○ _____

Diagnosis of Encopresis

- _____
- _____
- _____

Treatment and Management

- _____
- _____
- _____
- _____
- _____
- _____

Recommendations

- _____
- _____
- _____

ENURESIS

What is Enuresis?

- Most common type of elimination disorder
  - ○ _____
  - ○ _____
- _____
- _____

Causes of Enuresis

- _____
- _____
- _____
- _____
- _____
  _____

Notes

Diagnosis of Enuresis

- _____
- _____
- _____
- _____
- _____

Treatment and Management

- _____
- Bladder training: (Behavior 1st)
  - _____
  - _____
  - _____
- Rewards
  - _____
- _____
- _____

Recommendation

- _____
- _____
- _____
- _____

EPIGLOTTITIS

What is Epiglottitis

- _____
  _____
- Main bacteria: _____
- _____

Symptoms

- _____
- _____
- _____
- _____
- _____
- _____
- _____

Notes

- _____
- _____
- _____
- _____
- _____
- _____
- _____
- _____
- _____
- _____

Treatment and management

- _____
- _____
- _____

Recommendation

- _____
- _____
- _____

LACRIMAL DUCT

Lacrimal Duct

- _____
- _____

Concern

- _____
- _____
- _____
- _____
- _____

Notes

Causes of Lacrimal Duct

- _____
- _____
- _____
- _____
- _____
- _____
- _____
- _____
- _____

Signs And Symptoms

- _____
- _____
- _____
- _____
- _____
- _____

Management of Lacrimal Duct

- _____

NEONATAL CONJUNCTIVITIS

What is Neonatal Conjunctivitis

- _____
- _____
- _____

Causes of Neonatal Conjunctivitis

- Chemical irritants – _____
- N. gonorrhea – _____
- Chlamydia – _____

Notes

Presentation of Neonatal Conjunctivitis

- _____
- _____
- _____
- Gonorrhea – _____
- Pseudomonas – _____
- Chlamydia – _____

Treatment and Management

- _____
- Lab studies – _____
- _____

Medication of Neonatal Conjunctivitis

- _____
- _____
- _____
- _____

Management of Neonatal Conjunctivitis

- _____
- _____
- _____
- _____
- _____
- _____
- _____

FRAGILE X SYNDROME

Fragile X Syndrome
- Boys behavior
  - _____
  - _____
  - _____
  - _____
  - _____
  - _____

Notes

- Paying attention
  - _____
  - _____
  - _____
- _____
- _____
- _____
- _____
- _____
- _____
- _____
- _____
- Problems with
  - _____
  - _____
  - _____
- _____
- _____
- _____
- _____

Causes of Fragile X Syndrome

- _____

Diagnosis of Fragile X Syndrome

- Amniocentesis
  - _____
- Chorionic villus sampling (CVS)
  - _____

Treatment and management of Fragile X Syndrome

- Special education to help with learning
  - _____
  - _____
- _____
- _____
- _____
- _____
- _____
- _____

Recommendations

- _____
- _____

Notes

GYNECOMASTIA

Gynecomastia
- _____
- _____
- _____
- _____

Causes of Gynecomastia
- Imbalance between
  - _____
  - _____
- _____
- _____
- _____
- _____
- Medications
  - _____
  - _____
  - _____
  - _____
  - _____
- _____
- _____
- Tumors in
  - _____
  - _____
- _____
- _____

1st Line Medication
- Anti-estrogens
  - _____
  - _____
  - _____

Treatment and Management of Gynecomastia
- _____
- _____
- Aromatase inhibitors
  - _____
- _____

Notes

HAND FOOT MOUTH DISEASE

Clinical Presentation of Hand Foot Mouth Disease

- _____
- _____
- A red rash
    - _____
    - _____
    - _____
- Painful, red, blister-like
    - _____
    - _____
- _____
- _____
- _____
- _____
- _____

Causes of Hand Foot Mouth Disease

- _____
- Spreads by:
    - _____
    - _____
    - _____
    - _____
    - _____

Diagnosis of Hand Foot Mouth Disease
- By evaluating
    - _____
    - _____
    - _____
    - _____

Education of Hand Foot Mouth Disease

- _____
- _____
- _____
- _____

Treatment and Management of Hand Foot Mouth Disease

- _____
- _____
- _____

Notes

PEDIATRICS

- _____
- _____
- _____
- Drink cold beverages, such as
  - _____
  - _____
- Avoid acidic foods and beverages, such as
  - _____
  - _____
  - _____
- _____
- _____
- _____

INTUSSUSCEPTION

Intussusception
- _____
- _____
- _____
- _____

Causes of Intussusception
- _____
- It is caused by an abnormal growth such as
  - _____
  - _____

Diagnosis of Intussusception
- _____
- _____
- _____

Treatment and Management of Intussusception
- Initial Care
  - _____
  - _____
- Correcting the Intussusception
  - _____
  - _____

Notes

Recommendation
- _____
- _____

JAUNDICE

Where to Look Jaundice
- _____
- _____
- _____
- _____
- _____

Top to bottom

Why Jaundice Occurs
- _____
- _____
- _____

Causes of Jaundice
- _____
- _____
- _____
- _____
- _____
- _____
- _____

Diagnosis of Jaundice
- _____
- _____
- _____

Treatment and Management
- _____
- _____
- _____
- _____
- _____

Notes

KAWASAKI

Kawasaki
- The blood vessels inflamed, type of vasculitis
  - _____
- _____
- _____
- _____

Signs And Symptoms

- _____
- _____
- _____
- _____
- _____
- _____
- _____
- _____

Cause of Kawasaki
- Scientists haven't found an exact cause for Kawasaki disease. But they think it's probably linked to
  - _____
  - _____
  - Environmental factors such as:
    - _____
    - _____

Diagnosis and Investigations

- _____
- _____
- _____
- _____
- _____

1st Line Medication
- _____
- _____

Management and Education
- _____
- The goals of initial treatment are to
  - _____
  - _____

Notes

PEDIATRICS

- _____
- _____
- _____
- _____
- _____

Recommendation
- _____
- Follow up
    - _____
    - _____
    - _____
    - _____
- _____

KLINEFELTER'S

Causes of Klinefelter's
- Most common cause
    - _____
- Fewer symptoms
    - _____
- Rare and results in a severe form
    - _____

Signs And Symptoms
- _____
- _____
- _____
- _____
- _____
- _____
- _____
- _____
- _____
- _____
- _____

Concerns
- _____
- _____
- _____
- _____

Notes

Diagnosis of Klinefelter's

- _____
- _____
- _____
- _____

Management and Education

- _____
- _____
- _____
- _____
- _____
- _____

MARFAN SYNDROME

Marfan Syndrome

- _____
- _____
- _____
- _____
-
- Marfan syndrome most commonly affects
  - _____
  - _____
  - _____
  - _____
  - _____

Cause of Marfan Syndrome

- _____

Presentation

- _____
- _____
- _____
- _____
- _____

Notes

Diagnosis of Marfan Syndrome

- _____
- _____
- _____
- _____
- _____
- _____

Management and Education

- _____
- _____
- _____
- _____
- _____
- _____

Education and Recommendations

- _____
- _____
- Parents, teachers, and medical professionals work together and provide children:
    - _____
    - _____

MASTITIS

Mastitis

- _____
- _____
- _____
- _____
- _____
- _____
- _____
- _____

Notes

Causes of Mastitis

- _____
- _____
- _____
- _____

Diagnosis of Mastitis

- _____
- _____
- _____

1st Line Medication

- _____
- _____

Management and Education

- _____
- Consultation with an experienced lactation consultant:
  - _____
- _____

Education and Recommendation

- _____
- _____

MEASLES

Measles
- Acute viral illness that last 2-4 days with fever and the three C's:
  - _____
  - _____
  - _____

Causes of Measles

- _____
- _____
- _____
- _____
- _____

Notes

Presentation and Diagnosis

- _____
  _____
- _____
- _____
- _____
- _____
- _____
- Skin rash: _____

Treatment and Management Part 1

- _____
- _____
- _____
- _____
- _____
- _____
- _____

MILESTONES FOR TODDLERS

2 MONTHS

Social and Emotional Skills

- _____
- _____
- _____

Language Skills

- _____
- _____

Learning and Thinking Skills

- _____
- _____
- _____

Movement Skills

- _____
- _____

Notes

4 MONTHS

Social and Emotional Skills

- _____
- _____
- _____

Language Skills

- _____
- _____
- _____

Learning and Thinking Skills

- _____
- _____
- _____
- _____
- _____
- _____
- _____
- _____

Movement Skills

- _____
- _____
- _____
- _____
- _____
- _____
- _____

Notes

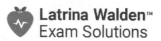

6 MONTHS

Social and Emotional Skills
- _____
- _____
- _____

Language Skills
- _____
- _____
- _____
- _____

Learning and Thinking Skills
- _____
- _____
- _____
- _____

Movement Skills
- _____
- _____
- _____
- _____

Notes

PEDIATRICS

9 MONTHS

Social and Emotional Skills

- _____
- _____
- _____

Language Skills

- _____
- _____
- _____
- _____

Learning and Thinking Skills

- _____
- _____
- _____
- _____
- _____
- _____

Movement Skills

- _____
- _____
- _____
- _____
- _____

Notes

1 YEAR

Social and Emotional Skills

- _____
- _____
- _____
- _____
- _____
- _____
- _____

Language Skills

- _____
- _____
- _____
- _____
- _____

Learning and Thinking Skills

- _____
- _____
- _____
- _____
- _____
- _____
- _____
- _____
- _____
- _____

Movement Skills

- _____
- _____
- _____
- _____

Notes

2 YEARS

Social and Emotional Skills

- _____
- _____
- _____
- _____
- _____

Language Skills

- _____
- _____
- _____
- _____
- _____

Learning and Thinking Skills

- _____
- _____
- _____
- _____
- _____
- _____
- _____
- _____

Movement Skills

- _____
- _____
- _____
- _____
- _____
- _____

Notes

3 YEARS

Social and Emotional Skills

- _____
- _____
- _____
- _____
- _____
- _____

Language Skills

- _____
- _____
- _____
- _____
- _____
- _____
- _____
- _____

Learning and Thinking Skills

- _____
- _____
- _____
- _____
- _____

Movement Skills

- _____
- _____
- _____
- _____

Notes

4 YEARS

Social and Emotional Skills

- _____
- _____
- _____
- _____
- _____

Language Skills

- _____
- _____
- _____
- _____

Learning and Thinking Skills

- _____
- _____
- _____
- _____
- _____
- _____
- _____

Movement Skill

- _____
- _____
- _____

Movement skills of Milestones for Toddlers

- _____
- _____
- _____
- _____
- _____
- _____
- _____

Hand and Finger Development

- _____
- _____
- _____

Notes

PEDIATRICS

MILIA

Milia
- _____
- _____
- _____
- _____

Causes of Milia
- _____
- _____

Diagnosis of Milia
- _____
- _____

Recommendation
- Avoid infection of Milia bumps
  - _____
  - _____
  - _____

MOLLUSCUM CONTAGIOSUM

Molluscum Contagiosum
- _____
- _____
- Word descriptions used:
  - _____
  - _____
  - _____
  - _____

Causes of Molluscum Contagiosum
- _____
- _____

Diagnosis of Molluscum Contagiosum
- _____
- _____
- _____

Notes

Treatment and Management
- _____
  - Cryotherapy
    - _____
  - Curettage
    - _____
  - Laser therapy
    - _____
  - Topical therapy
    - _____
    - _____

Education and Recommendation
- _____
  - Instruct children in proper hand-washing techniques
    - _____
    - _____
  - Avoid sharing personal items
    - _____
    - _____
    - _____
    - _____
- _____

NEPHROBLASTOMA

Nephroblastoma
- Kidney cancer
  - _____
- _____

Causes of Nephroblastoma
- _____

Diagnosis of Nephroblastoma
- _____
- _____
- _____
- _____
- _____

Treatment of Nephroblastoma
- _____
- _____
- _____

Notes

NEUROBLASTOMA

Neuroblastoma

- _____
  - Most commonly affects
    - _____
- _____
  - Neuroblastoma may spread:
    - _____
    - _____
    - _____

Signs and Symptoms of Neuroblastoma

- _____
- _____
- _____
- _____
- _____
- _____
- _____

Diagnosis of Neuroblastoma

- Physical exam – _____
- _____
- _____
- Removing a sample of tissue for testing - _____
- _____

Treatment of Neuroblastoma

- _____
- _____
- _____
- _____

Management and Education

- _____
- _____
- _____
- _____

Notes

PEDIATRICS

OSGOOD SCHLATTER

Osgood Schlatter
- Official:_____
  _____
- _____
- Occurs most often in children who participate in sports that involve running and jumping
  - _____
  - _____
  - _____
  - _____
  - _____
- _____

Causes and Signs/Symptoms of Osgood Schlatter
- _____
- _____
- _____
- _____

Diagnosis of Osgood Schlatter
- _____
- _____
- _____

Management
- _____
- _____
- _____

Patient Education
- _____
- _____
- _____
- _____
- _____
- _____
- _____

Notes

OTITIS MEDIA

Otitis Media
Infection:

- _____
- _____
- _____

Signs and Symptoms

- _____
- _____
- _____
- _____
- _____
- _____
- _____
- _____
- _____
- _____

Risk Factors of Otitis Media

- _____
- _____
- _____
- _____
- _____
- _____
- _____
- _____
- _____

Causes of Otitis Media

- URI due to:
  - _____
  - _____
  - _____

Diagnosis of Otitis Media

- _____
- _____

Notes

1ˢᵗ Line Medication

- _____
- _____
- _____

Management and Education

- _____
- _____
- Doctor may recommend antibiotic treatment in the following situations:
  - **Children 6 months and older:**
    - _____
    - _____
  - **Children 6 to 23 months:**
    - _____
    - _____
  - **Children 24 months and older**
    - _____
    - _____

PIAGET'S STAGES OF DEVELOPMENT

Stages:
- Sensorimotor stage
  - _____
  - _____
  - _____
  - _____
  - _____
  - _____
  - _____
  - _____
  - _____
  - _____
  - _____
- Preoperational stage
  - _____
  - _____
  - _____
  - _____
  - _____
  - _____
  - _____
  - _____
  - _____
  - _____

Notes

- Concrete operational stage
  - _____
  - _____
  - _____
  - _____
  - _____
  - _____
  - _____
  - _____
- Formal operational stage
  - _____
  - _____
  - _____

PRECOCIOUS PUBERTY

Precocious Puberty
- _____
- Considered
  - _____
  - _____
  - _____
- Physical Changes that need to draw concern:
  - _____
  - _____

Causes of Precocious Puberty
- Central Precocious Puberty
  - _____
  - _____
  - _____
  - _____
  - _____
  - _____
  - _____
- Peripheral Precocious Puberty
  - _____
  - _____
  - _____
  - _____
  - _____
  - _____
  - _____

Notes

Diagnosis of Precocious Puberty

- _____
- _____
- _____
- _____
- _____
- _____
- _____

Medications of Precocious Puberty

- _____

Management and Education

- _____
- _____
- _____

PRIMARY/ SECONDARY AMENORRHEA

Amenorrhea
- Primary Amenorrhea
  - _____
- Secondary amenorrhea
  - _____
    _____
- _____

Causes of Primary/ Secondary Amenorrhea
- Part 1:
  - _____
  - _____
  - _____
  - _____
  - _____
  - _____
  - _____
  - _____
- Part 2:
  - _____
  - _____
  - _____
  - _____
  - _____
  - _____

Notes

PEDIATRICS

- Other causes of hormonal problems
  - Long-term illness
    - _____
    - _____
  - _____
  - _____

Diagnosis of Primary/ Secondary Amenorrhea

- _____
- _____
- _____
- _____
- _____
- _____
- The following test should be individualized:
  - _____
  - _____
  - _____
  - _____
  - _____

Treatment and Management

- _____
- _____
- _____
- **Medical treatments for amenorrhea may include**
  - _____
  - _____
  - _____
- **Surgical treatments for amenorrhea may include**
  - _____
  - _____

PYLORIC STENOSIS

Pyloric Stenosis

- _____
- _____
- _____
- _____

Notes

Causes of Pyloric Stenosis
- _____
- _____
- Differentials:
    - _____
    - _____
    - _____
    - _____
    - _____
    - _____
    - _____

Diagnosis of Pyloric Stenosis
- Blood tests to check for
    - _____
    - _____
    - _____
- _____
- _____
- _____
- _____
- _____
- _____

Treatment and Management
- _____
- **Medical treatments may include**
    - _____
    - _____

RETINOBLASTOMA

Retinoblastoma
- _____
- _____
- _____
- _____
- _____

Causes of Retinoblastoma
- _____

Diagnosis of Retinoblastoma
    - _____
    - _____
    - _____

Notes

Education of Retinoblastoma
- _____

Treatment of Retinoblastoma
- _____
- _____
- _____
- _____
- _____
- _____
- _____

RH ANTIBODIES

Rh Antibodies
- _____
  _____
- _____
  _____
- _____
- _____

Cause of Rh Antibodies
- _____
  _____
- _____

Diagnosis of Rh Antibodies
- Rh factor blood test – coombs test_____

Management of Rh Antibodies
- _____
- _____
- _____
- _____
- _____

Recommendations
- _____
- _____
- _____
  _____
- _____

Notes

SCOLIOSIS

Scoliosis

- _____
  _____
- _____
- _____
- _____

- Severe scoliosis
  - _____
  - _____

Causes of Scoliosis
- Neuromuscular conditions, such as
  - _____
  - _____

- _____
- _____

Diagnosis of Scoliosis

- _____
- _____
- _____
- _____
- _____
- _____

Treatment and Management of Scoliosis
- Mild curves won't need treatment with a brace or surgery

  - _____
  - _____
  - _____
  - _____
  - _____

- Treatment depends on these factors
  - _____
  - _____
  - _____
  - _____
  - _____
  - _____
  - _____
  - _____
  - _____
  - _____
  - _____

Notes

PEDIATRICS

SIGN OF DEHYDRATION IN A BABY

Dehydration in a Baby

- _____
- _____
- _____
- _____
- _____
- _____
- _____
- _____

Mild to Moderate Dehydration

- _____
- _____
- _____
- _____
- _____
- If caused by diarrhea
  - _____
- _____
- _____

Severe Dehydration

- _____
- _____
- _____
- _____
- _____
- _____

Treatment of Dehydration

- _____
- _____
- _____
- _____
- _____

Notes

TANNER STAGES

Tanner Stages of Girls
- (Pubescent, Nothing) Stage 1:
  - _____
  - _____
- (Buds) Stage 2:
  - _____
  - _____
  - _____
- (Boobs) Stage 3:
  - _____
  - _____
  - _____
  - _____
- (Nips) Stage 4:
  - _____
  - _____
- (Mature) Stage 5:
  - _____
  - _____

Tanner Stages of Boys
- (Pubescent, Nothing) Stage 1:
  - _____
  - _____
- (Balls) Stage 2:
  - _____
  - _____
  - _____
- (Long) Stage 3:
  - _____
  - _____
  - _____
- (Wide) Stage 4:
  - _____
  - _____
  - _____
  - _____
  - _____
- (Mature) Stage 5:
  - _____
  - _____

Notes

TURNER'S SYNDROME

Causes of Turner's Syndrome
- _____
- _____

Concerns
- _____
- _____
- _____
- _____
- _____
- _____
- _____
- _____
- _____
- _____
- _____
- _____
- _____
- _____
- _____
- _____
- _____
- _____
- _____

Diagnosis of Turner's Syndrome
- _____
- _____
- _____
- _____
- _____
- _____

Management of Turner's Syndrome
- _____
- _____
- _____

Recommendation
- Most women and girls lead healthy and independent lives by taking
    - _____
    - _____

Notes

URINARY TRACT INFECTIONS (UTIS) IN CHILDREN

Urinary Tract Infections (UTIS) in Children
- Infection of the
    - _____
    - _____
- _____
- _____
- _____

Signs and Symptoms Include:
- _____
- _____
- _____
- _____
- _____
- _____

Causes Urinary Tract Infections (UTIS) in Children
- _____
- _____
- _____
- _____
- _____
- _____
- _____
- _____
- _____
- _____

Diagnosis of Urinary Tract Infections (UTIS) Children
- _____
- _____
- _____
- _____
- _____
- _____
- _____
- _____

Notes

1st Line Medication of Urinary Tract Infections (UTIS) Children
- _____
- _____
- _____
- _____

Treatment of Urinary Tract Infections (UTIS) Children
- _____
- _____
- Hospitalization may be necessary in cases where your child
  - _____
  - _____
  - _____
  - _____
  - _____

Recommendation
- _____
- _____

Notes

Notes

PSYCHIATRIC

PSYCHIATRY

Definition of Psychiatry
- _____
  _____

_____

ACUTE SEROTONIN SYNDROME

Definition of Serotonin Syndrome
- _____
  _____

- Serotonin Syndrome is characterized by
  - _____
  - _____

Serotonin syndrome caused by
- _____

Age groups of serotonin Syndrome
- Has been observed in _____ and _____

Medications for Serotonin Syndrome
- _____
- _____
- _____

Symptoms of Serotonin Syndrome
- _____
- _____
- _____
- _____
- _____
- _____
- _____

Treatment of Serotonin Syndrome
- Mild: _____
- Mod – Severe: _____

Notes

SEASONAL AFFECTIVE DISORDER

Definition of Seasonal Affective Disorder (SAD)

- _____
  _____

Seasonal Affective Disorder Occurs When

- _____
- _____
- _____
- _____

Treatments for Seasonal Affective Disorder

- _____
- _____
- _____

ANOREXIA

Definition of Anorexia

- _____
  _____

Sign and Symptoms of Anorexia

- _____
- _____
- _____
- _____
- _____
- _____

Notes

PSYCHIATRIC

ATYPICAL ANTIPSYCHOTICS

Definition of Atypical Antipsychotics

- _____
  _____
    - Before 1970: _____ Antipsychotics
    - After 1970: _____ Antipsychotics

Drug Treatments

- _____
- _____
- _____

Drug Characteristics

- _____
- _____
- _____
- _____
- _____
- _____

OTHER PSYCH MEDICATIONS

SSRIs:

- _____ (paroxetine hydrochloride)
    - Always first choice for _____ and _____
    - Causes _____ and _____
- _____ (sertraline) and _____ (citalopram):
    - Good for _____ and have few _____
- _____ (escitalopram):
    - Used to _____
- _____:
    - Used for _____ and _____

Do not mix with other _____ medications, such as _____

Notes

BIPOLAR DISORDER

Definition of Bipolar Disorder
- _____
- _____
  _____

Bipolar Disorder occurs
- _____ or _____

Categories of Bipolar Disorder
- _____
- _____
- _____

Symptoms
- _____
- _____
- _____
- _____
- _____
- _____
- _____
- _____

Stages of Bipolar Disorder
- _____
- _____
- _____
- _____
- _____

Treatments for Bipolar Disorder
- _____
- _____
- _____

Notes

PSYCHIATRIC

GENERALIZED ANXIETY DISORDER

Definition of Generalized Anxiety Disorder:

- _____
  _____

Symptoms:

- _____
- _____
- _____
- _____
- _____
- _____

Treatments:

- _____
- _____
- _____(bupropion)
    - Helps with _____ from SSRI/Paxil
    - Do not give to people with _____ or _____
- _____

ANXIETY (PANIC) ATTACK

Definition of Anxiety (Panic) Attack

- _____
  _____

Symptoms of Anxiety (Panic) Attack

- _____
- _____
- _____
- _____

Treatments for Anxiety (Panic) Attack

- _____: SHORT PERIOD OF TIME
- No _____ for the Elderly
- _____ – Herb Supplement

Notes

PSYCHIATRIC

ADHD BEHAVIOR

Definition of ADHD Behavior
- _____
  _____

Characteristics of ADHD Behavior
- _____
- _____

Effects of ADHD
- _____
- _____
- _____
- _____
- _____
- _____
- _____
- _____

Treatments for ADHD Behavior
- _____ is effective treatment for attention-deficit/hyperactivity disorder (ADHD)
  - It can improve _____, _____ and _____
- Therapy first, then _____ (List 5)
  - _____
  - _____
  - _____
  - _____
  - _____
- _____

ALCOHOLISM

Definition of Alcoholism
- _____
  _____

Treatment for Alcoholism
- _____
- _____

Notes

PSYCHIATRIC

Meaning of CAGE
- C: _____
- A: _____
- G: _____
- E: _____

Function of CAGE
- CAGE is a simple screening questionnaire to _____
  - _____ for family
  - _____ for teenagers and children

WERNICKE- KORSAKOFF DEMENTIA

Definition Wernicke- Korsakoff syndrome:
- _____
  _____

Causes of Wernicke- Korsakoff syndrome
- Lack of _____ (vitamin B1)
- _____ (MRC) + _____

Symptoms of Wernicke- Korsakoff syndrome
- _____
- _____
- _____
- _____
- _____

Pathology of WKS
- WKS occur in the following regions of brain:
  - _____
  - _____
  - _____
  - _____
  - _____
  - _____
  - _____

Notes

Definition Korsakoff Syndrome
- _____

  _____

Common Symptoms of Korsakoff syndrome
- _____
- _____
- _____

Characteristics of WKS
- It classically but not always presents with the clinical triad of _____,
  _____, and _____

Treatment of Korsakoff Syndrome
- _____

WHY PATIENTS STOP TAKING PSYCHOACTIVE DRUGS

Reasons:
- Men
  - _____
- Women
  - _____

Notes
```




```

PSYCHIATRIC

PULMONARY

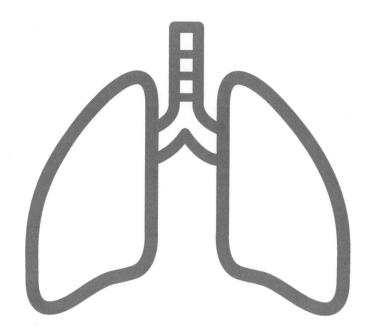

PNEUMONIA AND TB

How Do You Determine of The Patient Has Pneumonia or TB

- _____

_____

TUBERCULOSIS

Signs of Tuberculosis

- _____
- _____
- _____
- _____
- _____

How Does Tuberculosis Spread From One to Another?

_____

_____

Symptoms of Tuberculosis

- _____
- _____
- _____

Treatment of Tuberculosis

- Never do fewer than _____ to _____ drugs initially if positive, then you can narrow it down
- Latent TB usually treated with _____
- If you suspect active TB, order _____, _____, and _____. the AFB is not _____.
- Sputum for _____ is gold standard
  - Deep morning cough collected for _____
- TB is usually upper lobes
  - >5mm: _____
  - 10mm: _____
  - >15mm: _____
- CXR: shows _____

Notes

PNEUMONIA

Types of Pneumonia

- _____
- _____

What is the Difference Between Typical and Atypical Community-Acquired Pneumonia?
- Typical
  - Etiology: _____
  - Clinical Presentation: _____
  - Diagnosis gram stain: _____
  - Radiography: _____
  - Treatment with penicillin: _____
- Atypical
  - Etiology: _____
  - Clinical Presentation: _____
  - Diagnosis gram stain: _____
  - Radiography: _____
  - Treatment with penicillin: _____

Curb 65 Criteria
- Principal adverse prognostic factors present?
  - _____
  - Urea > _____ mmol/L
  - Respiratory rate ≥ _____ /min
  - Blood pressure (systolic < _____ mm Hg, diastolic ≤ _____ mm Hg)
  - Age ≥ _____ years

- 0-1 factor present
  - _____ CAP (risk of death < _____ %)
  - Consider other indications for hospital admission (_____, _____)
  - If yes, _____
  - If no, _____

- 2 factors present
  - _____ CAP (risk of death _____ %)
  - _____

- ≥3 factors present
  - _____ CAP (risk of death _____ % to _____ %)
  - Hospitalization consider admission to _____ especially if _____ to _____ factors are present.

Notes

CHRONIC OBSTRUCTIVE PULMONARY DISEASE (COPD)

Definition of COPD
- _____
  _____

Symptoms of COPD
- _____
- _____
- _____
- _____
- _____
- _____
- _____
- _____
- _____
- _____
- _____
- _____
- _____
- _____
- _____

Co-morbidity in COPD Exacerbations
- _____
- _____
- _____
- _____
- _____
- _____
- _____
- _____
- _____
- _____
- _____
- _____

Notes

Treatment of COPD
- Classification of airflow limitation severity
    - Gold 1 (mild)
        - Fev≥ _____% predicated
    - Gold 2 (moderate)
        - _____% ≤Fev< _____% predicted
    - Gold 3 (severe)
        - _____% ≤Fev< _____% predicated
    - Gold 4 (very severe)
        - Fev< _____% predicated

- Corresponding Medications
    - _____ with _____
    - _____/_____
    - _____/_____ with _____
    - Refer to _____

Medications
- SABA:
    - _____
    - _____
- Anticholinergic:
    - _____
- LABA:
    - _____
    - _____

Recommendations and Long-Term Treatment
- _____
- _____

Notes

HYPERCAPNIA

Definition and Causes of Hypercapnia

- _____
  _____

Main Symptoms of Hypercapnia

- Visual
  - _____
- Central
  - _____
  - _____
  - _____
  - _____
  - _____
- Auditory
  - _____
- Skin
  - _____
- Respiratory
  - _____
- Heart
  - _____
- Muscular
  - _____

EMPHYSEMA

Definition of Emphysema

- _____
  _____

Symptoms of Emphysema

- _____
- _____
- _____
- _____
- _____
- _____

Normal Bronchiole and alveoli VS Affected Alveoli

- _____
  _____

Notes

ASTHMA

Classification of Asthma?
- _____
  _____

Symptoms of Asthma
- _____
- _____
- _____
- _____

Key Triggers of Asthma
- _____
- _____
- _____
- _____
- _____
- _____

Assessing severity and Initiating therapy in children who are taking long term control medication
- Determining Factor of Severity
  - _____
- Symptoms
  - _____
  - _____
  - _____
- Risks
  - _____
- Classification of Asthma severity
  - _____
  - _____ (3 Levels)
    - _____
    - _____
    - _____
  - Recommended steps for initiating therapy
    - Step 1: _____
    - Step 2: _____
    - Step 3: _____

Notes

PULMONARY

EXERCISE- INDUCED ASTHMA

Definition of Exercise-Induced Asthma
- _____
  _____

Treatment steps for EIB:
- _____
- Add low dose _____
- Add _____
  - Never Add before step 3
- Add medium dose _____

Notes

Notes

_____
_____
_____
_____
_____
_____
_____
_____
_____
_____
_____
_____
_____
_____
_____
_____
_____
_____
_____
_____
_____
_____
_____
_____
_____
_____
_____
_____
_____
_____
_____
_____
_____

SKIN

ABOUT SKIN

Definition of Skin

- _____
  _____

Classification of Skin Disease

- _____
- _____
- _____
- _____
- _____
- _____
- _____
- _____

Functions of Skin

- _____
- _____
- _____
- _____
- _____
- _____
- _____
- _____
- _____

ROCKY MOUNTAIN SPOTTED FEVER

Definition of Rocky Mountain Spotted Fever

- _____
  _____

Symptoms of Rocky Mountain Spotted Fever

- _____
- _____
- _____
    - Photophobia and Long-term damage = _____

Diagnosis of Rocky Mountain Spotted Fever

- _____
- _____
- _____
- _____

Notes

SKIN

Treatment of Rocky Mountain Spotted Fever
- _____
- _____
  - What is Doxycycline? _____

ERYTHEMA MIGRAINES

Definition of Erythema Migraines
- _____
  _____

What Does an Erythema Migraine Look Like?
- _____
  _____

Symptoms of Erythema Migraines
- _____
- Target bullseye
  - _____
  - _____

Diagnosis of Erythema Migraines
- _____
- _____
- _____

Treatment of Erythema Migraines
- Patients age < 7
  - _____
    OR
  - _____
- Patients age > 7
  - _____

MELANOMA

What is Melanoma?
- _____
  _____

Notes

_____
_____
_____
_____
_____
_____

How Does a Melanoma Develop?

- _____
- _____

What Does it Look Like?

- _____
- _____
- _____
- _____
- _____
- _____
- _____
- _____
- _____
- _____

Stages of Melanoma

- _____
- _____

Melanoma < _____ mm

STEVENS JOHNSON SYNDROME

Definition of Stevens Johnson Syndrome

- _____
  _____

Symptoms of Stevens Johnson Syndrome
- Classic is target or bullseye
  - _____
  - _____
  - _____
  - _____
  - _____
  - _____

Cautions of Stevens Johnson Syndrome

- _____
- _____
- _____
- _____

Notes

PSORIASIS

Definition of Psoriasis
- _____
  _____

Symptoms of Psoriasis
- _____
  - Pruritic erythematous plaques, fine silvery-white scales with pitted fingernails
    - _____
    - _____
    - _____
    - _____
    - _____

Treatment of Psoriasis
- _____
- _____
- _____
- _____

ACANTHROS NIGRICANS

Definition of Acanthros Nigricans
- _____
  _____

Signs and Symptoms of Acanthros Nigricans
- _____
- _____

Related Disease
- _____
- _____
- _____
- _____

Notes

SCABIES

Definition of Scabies
- _____
  _____

Causes of Scabies
- _____
- _____
- _____

Treatment of Scabies
- Wash bed sheets and everything else in hot water
  _____
- Permethrin cream:
  - _____
  - _____
  - _____

ATOPIC DERMATITIS (ECZEMA)

Definition of Atopic Dermatitis (Eczema)
- _____
  _____

Symptoms of Atopic Dermatitis (Eczema)
- _____
- On flexural folds, neck, hands, groin, finger and toe webs.
  - Small vesicles that-
    - _____
    - _____
    - _____

Examination of Atopic Dermatitis (Eczema)
- _____
- _____

Treatment of Atopic Dermatitis (Eczema)
- _____
- _____
- _____

Notes

SKIN

TINEA CORPORIS

What is Tinea Corporis?
- _____
  _____

Treatment of Tinea Corporis
- Most respond
  - _____
- In severe condition
  - _____

ACTINIC KERATOSIS

Definition of Actinic Keratosis
- _____
  _____

How to grow Actinic Keratosis
- _____

Diagnosis of Actinic Keratosis
- _____

Treatment of Actinic Keratosis
- _____
- (5-FU cream)- which causes skin to
  - _____
  - _____
  - _____
  - _____

SEBORRHEIC KERATOSIS

Definition of Seborrheic Keratosis
- _____
  _____

What Does it Look Like?
- _____
- _____
- _____

Nature of This Disease
- _____
- _____

Notes

CELLULITIS

Definition of Cellulitis

- _____

Signs of Cellulitis

- _____
- _____
- _____

Treatment of Cellulitis

- _____
- Monitor the infection
    - Better
    - Worse
    Get medical care immediately if:
        - _____
        - _____
        - _____

Examination

- _____
- _____

ERYSIPELAS

Definition of Erysipelas

- _____

Treatment of Erysipelas

- _____
- _____
- _____
- _____

If allergic to Penicillin, then use Azithromycin x5d

Notes

MRSA AND BASAL CELL CARCINOMA

Definition of MRSA and Basal Cell Carcinoma
- _____
  _____

MRSA Classification
- _____
- _____
- _____
- _____
- _____
- MRSA infections
  - People who've been in hospitals or other health care settings-
    - _____
    - _____

Treatment of MRSA and Basal Cell Carcinoma
- _____
- _____
- _____
- _____

If sulfa allergy, do not use Bactrim

MOLLOSCUM CONTAGIOSUM

Definition Molloscum Contagiosum
- _____
  _____

Effect of Molloscum Contagiosum
- Upper layer of the skin
  - _____
  - _____

What Does it Look Like?
- _____
- _____

Nature of Molloscum Contagiosum
- _____

Notes

VARICELLA ZOSTER VIRUS

Definition of Varicella
- _____
  _____

Symptoms of Varicella
- _____
- _____
- _____
- _____
- _____
- _____

Treatment of Varicella
- _____
- _____
- _____

ACNE VULGARIS (COMMON ACNE)

Definition of Acne Vulgaris (Common Acne)
- _____
  _____

Treatment of Acne Vulgaris (Common Acne)
- Retin-A, acne worsens
  - _____
    Or add
  - _____
  - _____
- Moderate (topicals plus antibiotics)-
  - _____
  - _____
- Continue with topical combined with topical antibiotics
- Then add ORAL antibiotics:
  - _____
  - _____
  - _____

Notes

- Severe- with painful indurated
    - _____
    - _____
    - _____
    - _____
- Accutane- check LFTs
    - _____
    - _____
    - _____

ACNE ROSACEA

Definition of Acne Rosacea
- _____
  _____

Treatment of Acne Rosacea
- _____
- _____
- _____

IMPETIGO AND SCARLET FEVER

Definition of Impetigo and Scarlet Fever
- _____
  _____

Treatment of Impetigo and Scarlet Fever
- _____
- _____
- If allergic to penicillin, then:
    - _____
    - _____
- If NO BULLAE- _____

Symptoms of Impetigo and Scarlet Fever
- _____
- _____
- _____
- _____
- _____

Notes

LICHEN PLANUS

Definition of Lichen Planus
- _____
  _____

Causes of Lichen Planus
- _____
- _____

Treatment of Lichen planus
- _____
- _____

SPIDER BITE

What is a Spider Bite?
- _____
  _____

Symptoms of Spider Bite
- _____
- _____
- _____
- _____

Treatment of Spider Bite
- _____
- _____
- _____
- _____

PITYRIASIS ROSEA

Definition of Pityriasis Rosea
- _____
  _____

Notes

SKIN

What Does Pityriasis Rosea Look Like?

- _____
- _____
- _____
- _____

Treatment of Pityriasis Rosea

- _____
- _____
- _____

How Long Does it Take for Pityriasis Rosea to Go Away?

- _____

MONGOLIAN SPOTS AND KAWASAKI DISEASES

Definition of Mongolian Spots Disease

- _____
  _____

Definition of Kawasaki Disease

- _____

Symptoms of Mongolian Spots and Kawasaki Diseases

- _____
- _____
- _____

Treatment of Mongolian Spots and Kawasaki Diseases

- _____
- _____

Notes

HERPETIC KERATOSIS/KERATITIS

Definition of Herpetic Keratosis/ Keratitis
- _____
  _____

Symptoms of Herpetic Keratosis/ Keratitis
- _____
- _____
- _____

How does Herpetic Keratosis/ Keratitis Aggravate?
- _____

Consequences
- _____

Notes

Notes

SKIN

WOMEN'S – HEALTH PREGNANCY

Latrina Walden™
Exam Solutions

Presumptive Signs of Pregnancy

- _____
- _____
- _____
- _____
- _____
- _____
- _____

Probable Signs of Pregnancy

- _____
- _____
- _____
- _____
- _____
- _____
- _____
- _____

Positive Signs of Pregnancy

- _____
- _____
- _____
- _____

HOW TO DETERMINE IF MEMBRANES HAVE RUPTURED

Symptoms & Signs

- _____
- _____
- _____
- _____
- _____

What Tests Can Be Ran?

- _____
- _____
- _____
- _____
- _____

Notes

- Tests measure the levels of the following chemicals:
  - _____
  - _____
  - _____
  - _____

- _____ levels of these substances mean that the membranes have broken

_____

GOODELL'S SIGN

What Does the Goodell Sign Indicate?

- _____

Characteristics of Goodell Sign
- It is a significant _____ of the vaginal portion of the _____ from increased
  _____

Definition of Vascularization

- _____
  _____

_____

CHADWICK'S SIGN

Definition of Chadwick's Sign

- _____
  _____

When Does it Appear?

- _____

How Can it Be Observed?

- _____

HEGAR'S SIGN

Definition of Hegar's Sign

- _____
  _____

Notes

FUNDAL HEIGHT LANDMARK

1st Trimester
- _____

2nd Trimester
- _____

3rd Trimester
- _____
- At 37–40 weeks
  - _____

PREGNANCY APPOINTMENT SCHEDULE

Weeks 4 to 28
- _____

Weeks 28 to 36
- _____

Weeks 36 to 40
- _____

NAEGELE'S RULE

How is Naegele's rule calculated?
- Naegele's rule involves a simple calculation:
  - Add _____ to the first day of your LMP
  - Then _____ months
  - Finally, _____

UTI DURING PREGNANCY

Risks of a UTI During Pregnancy
- _____
- _____
- _____
- _____
- _____
- _____
- _____
- _____
- _____
- _____

Notes

Causes of a UTIs During Pregnancy
- _____
- _____

Tests to Diagnose a UTI During Pregnancy
- _____
- _____

Medication for a UTI During Pregnancy
- First and second trimester
  - _____
- Second trimester
  - _____
- Third trimester
  - _____

MASTITIS

Definition of Mastitis
- _____
  _____

Symptoms and Side Effects of Mastitis
- _____
- _____
- _____
- _____
- _____
- _____
- _____

Causes of Mastitis
- _____
- _____

Diagnosis of Mastitis
- _____
- Cultures may be taken through a syringe from
  - _____
  - _____
- _____
- _____

Notes

Medication for Mastitis
- 1ˢᵗ Line medication
    - _____

Management and Education of Mastitis
- Part 1
    - Take all antibiotics as prescribed
    - Take your _____ _____ times a day for the first _____ hours after treatment begins.
    - Call your doctor if you develop
        - _____
        - _____
        - _____
        - _____
        - _____
- Part 2
    - Follow up with your doctor in _____ to _____ weeks
    - If the infection spreads or an _____ develops, you may require _____ or _____
    - Surgery is required if _____. It must be _____.

PLACENTA PREVIA

Risks of Placenta Previa
- _____
- _____
- _____

Cause of Placenta Previa
- _____

Risks Factors of Placenta Previa
- If you have scars on the uterus, from sources such as
    - _____
    - _____
    - _____
    - _____
- _____
- _____
- _____
- _____
- _____
- _____

Diagnosis of Placenta Previa
- _____

Notes

Treatment of Placenta Previa

- _____
- _____

Control Bleeding
- For little or no bleeding
  - _____
  - _____
- For heavy bleeding
  - Severe bleeding might require _____
  - Plan a _____ as soon as the baby _____
  - If your delivery is planned before _____ weeks, your doctor will offer you _____ to help your baby's lungs develop
- For bleeding that won't stop
  - _____ — even if the baby _____

Management & Education

- _____
- _____
- _____
- _____

PLACENTA ABRUPTION

Risks of Placenta Abruption

- _____
- _____
- _____
- _____
- _____
- _____
- _____
- _____
- _____
- _____
- _____
- _____
- _____

Cause of Placenta Abruption

- _____
- _____

Notes

Diagnosis of Placenta Abruption

- _____
- _____
- _____
- _____

Treatment Part 1
- Baby's heart rate is normal, and it is too early for the baby to be born
    - _____
- Bleeding stops and your baby's condition is stable
    - _____

Treatment Part 2
- Given _____ to help baby's lungs mature and protect brain
- If the abruption worsens or jeopardizes your or your baby's health
    - _____

Recommendations

- _____
- _____
- _____

PREECLAMPSIA

Risks of Preeclampsia

- _____
- _____
- _____
- _____
- _____
- _____
- _____
- _____
- _____

Causes of Preeclampsia

- _____
- _____
- _____
- _____

Notes

Diagnosis of Preeclampsia

- _____
- _____
- _____
- _____
- _____
- _____
- _____
- _____
- _____
- _____

Medications for Preeclampsia

- _____
- _____
- _____

Management of Preeclampsia

- _____
- _____
- _____

ECLAMPSIA

Risks of Eclampsia

- _____
- _____
- _____
- _____
- _____
- _____
- _____

Cause of Eclampsia

- _____

Diagnosis of Eclampsia

- _____
- _____
- _____

Notes

Medications for Eclampsia
- _____

Management of Eclampsia
- Treatment for preeclampsia and eclampsia
    - _____
    - _____
- Mild preeclampsia
    - _____

RH ANTIBODIES

Suggest Doing Them or Give if
- _____
- _____

Risk is Higher for Pregnant Women with a History of
- _____
- _____
- _____
- _____
- _____
- _____
- _____
- _____
- _____
- _____
- _____
- _____
- _____
- _____

Diagnosis of Rh Antibodies
- _____

Notes

Medications of Rh Antibodies
- Preventive: _____

Management of Rh Antibodies
- _____
- _____
- _____
- _____
- _____

Recommendations of Rh Antibodies
- For _____ during pregnancy, contact your health care provider immediately
- Talk with your health care provider about scheduling an _____ during your pregnancy and remind of your Rh status during labor

---

AFP BLOOD TEST DURING PREGNANCY
- Unborn babies normally make _____ (AFP)
- It shows up in _____
- AFP only tells you _____, not _____
- A negative or normal test means the baby _____
- A positive test with a high AFP suggests _____
- A positive test with low AFP could mean _____

TRIPLE TEST
- _____
- _____
- _____

QUAD SCREEN

Measures
- _____
- _____
- _____
- _____

When is This Performed?
- _____

Notes

This Test Evaluates Chance Of Carrying

- _____
- _____
- _____
- _____

GROUP B STREP TEST

Characteristics of the Group B Strep Test

- A group B strep test recommended during the _____ trimester
- A swab from _____ and _____ are sent to a lab for testing
- Used to identify women who carry _____
- If the group B strep test is negative, _____
- If the group B strep test is positive, _____

Group B Strep Can Cause:

- _____
- _____
- _____
- _____
- _____

ORAL CONTRACEPTIVES AND CONTRAINDICATIONS

3 Types:

- _____ birth control pills
- _____ birth control pills
- _____ birth control pills

Relative Contraindications to Contraceptives Include:

- _____
- _____
- _____
- _____
- _____
- _____
- _____
- _____
- _____

Notes

Latrina Walden™
Exam Solutions

Absolute Contraindications Include:

- _____
- _____
- _____
- _____
- _____
- _____

Notes

Additional Notes

Additional Notes

Bronze Clinical Crash Course Notes

Additional Notes

Additional Notes

Additional Notes

Additional Notes

Additional Notes

Additional Notes

Additional Notes

Additional Notes

Index

OLFACTORY
OPTIC
OCULOMOTOR
TROCHLEAR
TRIGEMINAL
ABDUCENS
FACIAL
VESTIBULOCOCHLEAR
GLOSSOPHARYNGEAL
VAGUS
ACCESSORY
HYPOGLOSSAL
NEUROLOGY DISORDER
MIGRAINE
CLUSTER HEADACHES
ESSENTIAL TREMORS
BENIGN PAROXYSMAL POSITIONAL VERTIGO
FIBROMYALGIA
SUBARACHNOID HEMORRHAGE
SUBDURAL HEMORRAGE
TRIGEMINAL NEURALGIA
POLYMYALGIA RHEUMATICA
TEMPORAL ARTERITIS
CARPAL TUNNEL SYNDROME
ABSENCE SEIZURE
ALZHEIMER'S DISEASE
LEWY BODY DEMENTIA
VASCULAR DEMENTIA
SYNCOPE
TENSION HEADACHES
MENINGITIS
STROKE
TRANSIENT ISCHEMIC ATTACK (TIA)
BELL'S PALSY
EPILEPSY
PARKINSON'S DISEASE
MULTIPLE SCLEROSIS
DELIRIUM
NEUROFIBROMATOSIS

PEDIACTRICS
5TH DISEASE
ADHD
AUTISM
BRONCHIOLITI
CAPUT SUCCEDANEUM
CEPHALOHEMATOMA
CLOSING OF FONTANEL
COARCTATION OF AORTA
CROUP
CYANOSIS
ENCOPRESIS
ENURESIS
EPIGLOTTITIS
LACRIMAL DUCT

NEONATAL CONJUNCTIVITIS
FRAGILE X SYNDROME
GYNECOMASTIA
HAND FOOT MOUTH DISEASE
INTUSSUSCEPTION
JAUNDICE
KAWASAKI
KLINEFELTER'S
MARPHANS SYNDROME
MASTITIS
MEASLES
MILESTONES FOR TODDLERS
MILIA
MOLLUSCUM CONTAGIOSUM
NEPHROBLASTOMA
NEUROBLASTOMA
OSGOOD-SCHLATTER
OTITIS MEDIA
PIAGET'S STAGES OF DEVELOPMENT
PRECOCIOUS PUBERTY
PRIMARY/SECONGDARY AMENORRHEA
PYLORIC STENOSIS
RETINOBLASTOMA
RH ANTIBODIES
SCOLIOSIS
SIGN OF DEHYDRATION IN A BABY
STOMATITIS
TANNER STAGES
TURNER'S SYNDROME
URINARY TRACT INFECTIONS (UTIS) IN CHILDREN

PSYCHIATRY

ACUTE SEROTONIN SYNDROME
SEASONAL AFFECTIVE DISORDER
ANOREXIA
ATYPICAL ANTIPSYCHOTICS
OTHER PSYCHO MEDICATIONS
BIPOLAR
GENERALIZED ANXIETY DISORDER
ANXIETY (PANIC) ATTACK
ADHD BEHAVIOR
ALCOHOLICS
WERNICKE- KORSAKOFF DEMENTIA
WHY PATIENTS STOP TAKING PSYCHOACTIVE DRUGS

PULMONARY

WHERE DOES IT SHOW FOR PNEUMONIA OR TB
TUBERCULOSIS
PNEUMONIA
CHRONIC OBSTRUCTIVE PULMONARY DISEASE (COPD)
HYPERCAPNIA
EMPHYSEMA LUNGS
ASTHMA
EXERCISE- INDUCED ASTHMA
QUAD SCREEN
GROUP B STREP TEST

ORAL CONTRACEPTIVES AND CONTRAINDICATIONS

SKIN

ABOUT SKIN
ROCKY MOUNTAIN SPOTTED FEVER
ERYTHEMA MIGRAINES
MELANOMA
STEVENS JOHNSON SYNDROME
PSORIASIS
ACANTHROS NIGRICANS
SCABIES
ATOPIC DERMATITIS (ECZEMA)
TINEA CORPORIS
ACTINIC KERATOSIS
SEBORRHEIC KERATOSIS
CELLULITIS
ERYSIPELAS
MRSA AND BASAL CELL CARCINOMA
MOLLOSCUM CONTAGIOSUM
VARICELLA ZOSTER VIRUS
ACNE VULGARIS (COMMON ACNE)
ACNE ROSACEA
IMPETIGO AND SCARLET FEVER
LICHEN PLANUS
SPIDER BITE
PITYORIS ROSEA
MONGOLIAN SPOTS AND KAWASAKIDISEASES
HERPETIC KERATOSIS/KERATITIS

WOMAN'S HEALTH

SIGN OF PREGNANCY
HOW TO DETERMINE IF MEMBRANES HAVE RUPTURED
GOODELL'S SIGN
CHADWICK'S SIGN
HEGAR'S SIGN
FUNDAL HEIGHT LANDMARK
PREGNANCY APPOINTMENT SCHEDULE
NAEGELE'S RULE
UTI DURING PREGNANCY
MASTITIS
PLACENTA PREVIA
PLACENTA ABRUPTION
PREECLAMPSIA
ECLAMPSIA
RH ANTIBODIES
AFP BLOOD TEST DURING PREGNANCY
TRIPLE TEST
QUAD SCREEN
GROUP B STREP TEST
ORAL CONTRACEPTIVES AND CONTRAINDICATIONS

Acknowledgements

For Robert. Always being my safe space to land.

About Professor Walden

Latrina Walden is the Founder and CEO of Latrina Walden ™ Exam Solutions. Latrina has established herself as the go-to expert in the nursing industry. She has over 20 years of experience as a nursing home administrator, dialysis nurse, administration nurse, emergency room nurse, and family nurse practitioner. Latrina has dedicated the last decade of her career to education, bringing her passion and expertise in family and nursing to university and online classrooms. Latrina's extensive knowledge in the nursing industry, her academic experience, and her dedication to the nursing community has led her to identify major disconnects between university curriculums and real-world practice. As a modern-day pioneer, Latrina bridges this gap by teaching easy-to-digest strategies through pre-recorded videos and live interactive tutoring sessions. These fun and concise courses have supported graduate candidates across the U.S and Canada as they prepare to pass their certified nurse practitioner exams. Now, Latrina is expanding her business to help nurse practitioners navigate the full lifecycle of their career. Through her signature Nurse Practitioner Bridge Formula, Latrina provides the necessary study skills to support aspiring nurse practitioners in passing their certification exams and gives graduates the tools to operate as independent thinkers and confident providers in the industry.

"We are nurses supporting nurses – that's why this works." – Latrina Walden

www.latrinawaldenexamsolutions.com

About Professor Walden

Made in United States
Orlando, FL
14 July 2023

35097633R00157